Mapping Penny's World

For my parents, Grace and Jim,
who showed us the way

And in memory of the real Penny,
the longtime companion of my aunt Lorraine Stewart

ISBN 0-439-28596-8

Copyright © 2000 by Loreen Leedy. All rights reserved.
Published by Scholastic Inc., 555 Broadway, New York, NY 10012,
by arrangement with Henry Holt and Company, LLC. SCHOLASTIC and
associated logos are trademarks and/or registered trademarks of Scholastic Inc.

12 11 10 9 8 7 6 5 4 3 2 1   1 2 3 4 5 6/0

Printed in the U.S.A.   14

First Scholastic printing, November 2001

The artist combined digital painting and photo collage in Adobe Photoshop
to create the illustrations for this book.

Mapping Penny's World

written and illustrated by
Loreen Leedy

SCHOLASTIC INC.
New York Toronto London Auckland Sydney
Mexico City New Delhi Hong Kong Buenos Aires

My name is Lisa, and my class is making maps this month.

My teacher, Mr. Jayson, says a map is a picture of someplace from above. It's like flying over that spot in an airplane.

Mr. Jayson says we can make a map of anyplace—like a room, a yard, or a neighborhood.

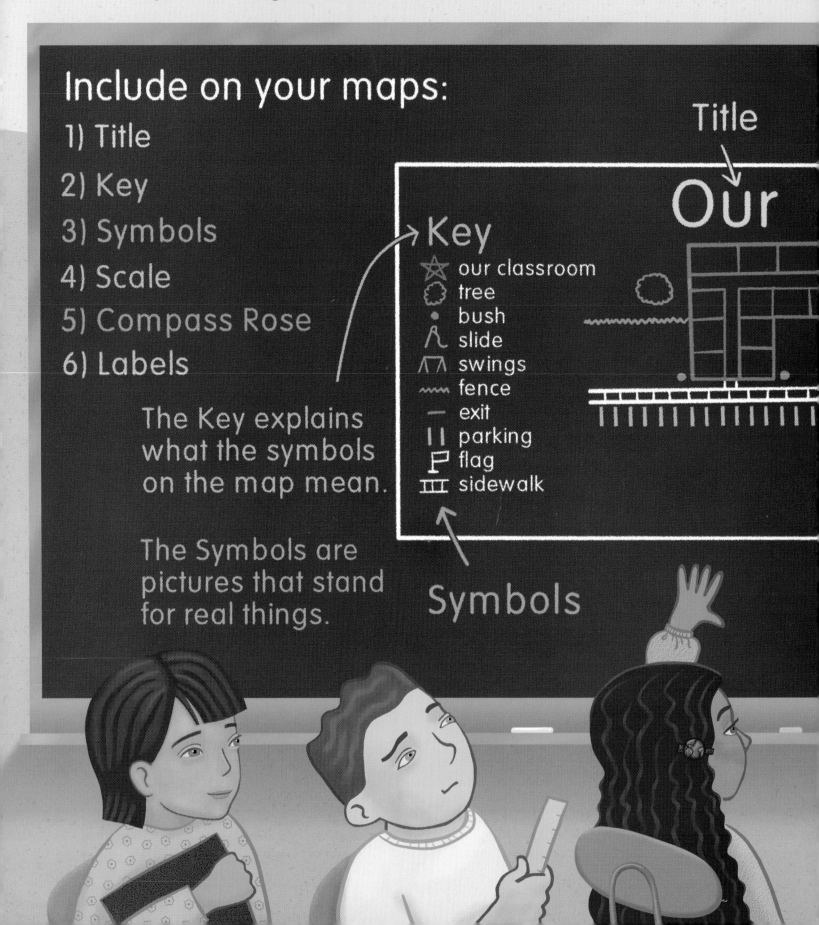

Include on your maps:
1) Title
2) Key
3) Symbols
4) Scale
5) Compass Rose
6) Labels

The Key explains what the symbols on the map mean.

The Symbols are pictures that stand for real things.

Title

Our

Key
☆ our classroom
🌳 tree
• bush
⋀ slide
⋀⋀ swings
〰 fence
— exit
‖ parking
⚑ flag
⊥⊥⊥ sidewalk

Symbols

Maybe I could make a map of my bedroom at home.

I'll measure my room and everything in it to make my map. Of course, I'll have to include Penny's bed. Penny is my Boston terrier and she sleeps in here, too.

Do you want to measure the fish tank, Penny?

My map shows how my bedroom would look from overhead, as if I were looking down from the ceiling.

My Bedroom
by Lisa

bed

rug

plant

bookshelf

That is a close-up map of the fish tank.
Thanks for your help, Penny!

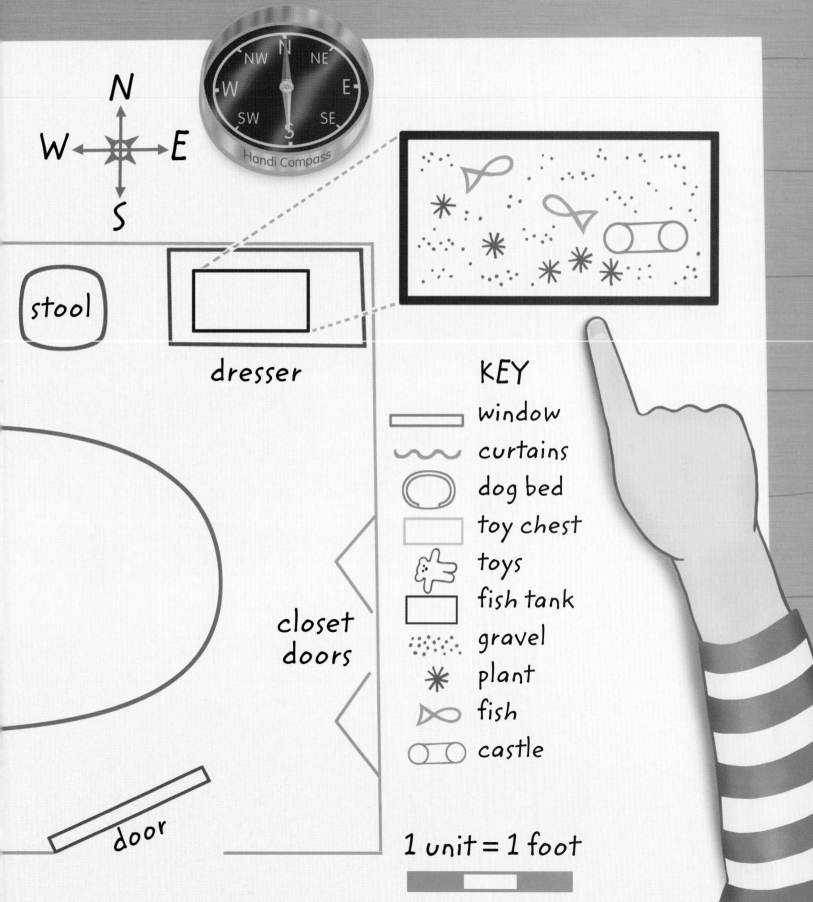

N
W   E
S

NW N NE
W   E
SW S SE
Handi Compass

stool

dresser

closet
doors

door

KEY
window
curtains
dog bed
toy chest
toys
fish tank
gravel
plant
fish
castle

1 unit = 1 foot

Penny likes to hide her toys and other stuff in the yard. I have found shoes and socks in the strangest places! Maybe I'll make a map of Penny's hideouts.

On this map, some of the symbols stand for the goodies she has hidden outside. The rest of the symbols represent the fence, table, and other things that are supposed to be out there. Penny, if you hide my doll, you'll be in BIG trouble.

Penny's
KEY
bone

squeaky toy

shoe

sock

buried underground

fence

birdbath

stepping-stone

trash can

brick path

table

chair

grass

bush

cement

Treasure Map

↑ **N**orth

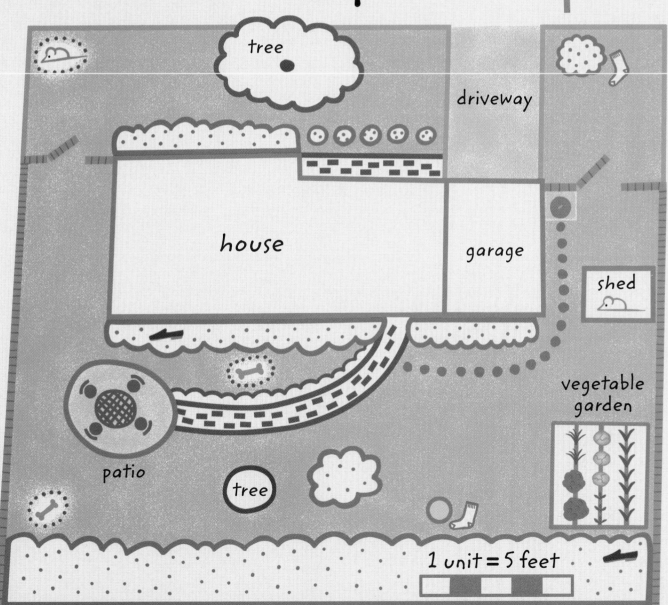

tree

driveway

house

garage

shed

patio

tree

vegetable garden

1 unit = 5 feet

Maps are good for giving directions. Suppose Penny's friend Maxine wants to come over. You could say, "Go out your back door, turn right by the trash cans, crawl under the gap in the wooden fence (watch out for the big orange cat!), squeeze through the bushes,

turn left, look for the yellow fire hydrant, turn right on the sidewalk, go to the third house on the right with the red door, sit down in front of it, and bark." Whew! Or you could draw a map instead.

Here is the shortest way from Maxine's house to our house.

Maxine's Route

KEY

- .... Maxine's path
- ☐ house
- ⊒ wood fence
- ◎ trash can
- ☁ bush
- ▦ sidewalk
- ⊙ fire hydrant
- 🐱 cat

neighbor's house

Maxine's house

Latitude Avenue

It's a lot longer if you go around the block, instead of going the back way.

to Our House

N
W E
S

Roving Road

our house

1 unit = 20 feet

Longitude Street

I can't take Maxine when I ride my bike, because there's only room for Penny in the basket.

These are our trails. To make this map, I measured our foot paths with a pedometer, a tool that shows how far a person walks. For the bike trails, I used an odometer, which shows how far a vehicle travels.

Our Hike and

KEY

—— bike trail

- - - foot path

~~~ river

▨ bridge

▲ forest

⌒ hill

▬ road

🪑 picnic table

R restrooms

River Road

Legend Lake

A•

STEPCOUNTER
PEDOMETER
0.2 MILES
RESET SET MODE

The map's scale shows the real distances in the park. According to the map, the distance between point A and point B is two-tenths of a mile.

Bike Trails

Forest Lane

North

R

1/10 mile

B

Park Avenue

When we go out into the neighborhood, Penny has some favorite places she likes to visit again and again.

I made this three-dimensional map with construction paper and clay. The numbers show where Penny can do different activities.

Penny's Favorite Places

Main Street

6

KEY
1. watch turtles and ducks
2. bark at squirrels
3. beg for new toys
4. smell food
5. meet other dogs
6. rest in the shade
7. fetch sticks

1 unit = 5 feet

1

N
W   E
S

Penny loves to travel outside our neighborhood, too. I think there are special places she would enjoy visiting, like a doggie treat factory, a really huge park, or a big dog show.

BEST IN SHOW

This map shows a few of the places Penny can go . . .

. . . and I'm going with her.

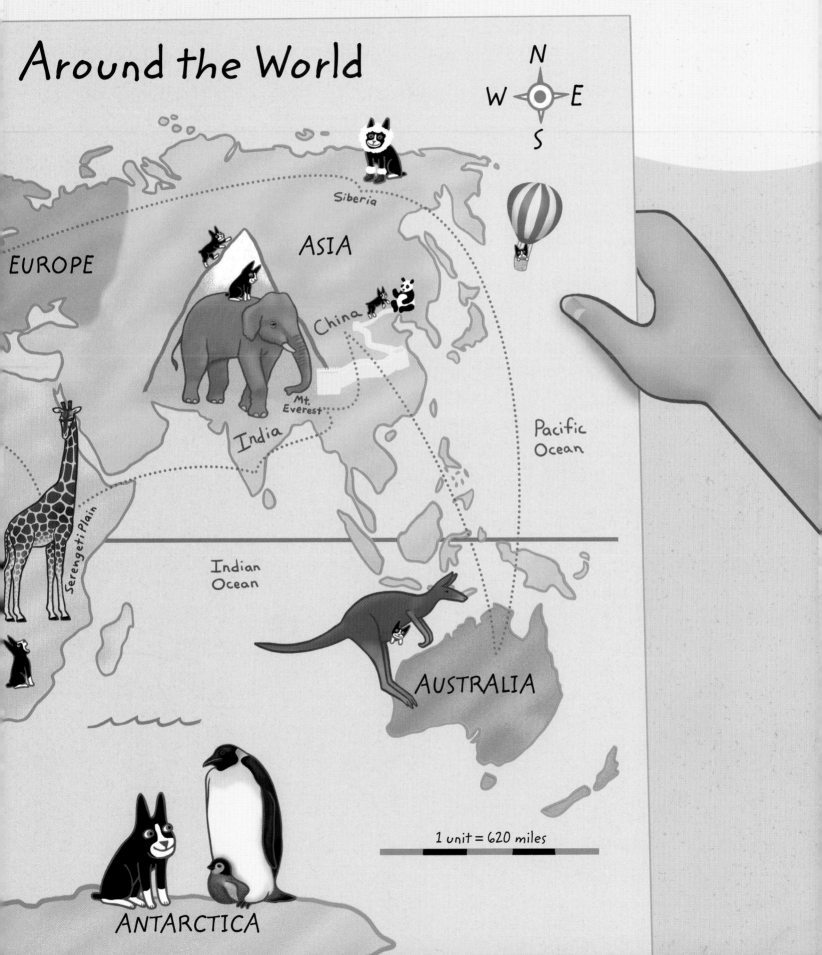

Don't forget the maps, Penny!

July 2002

The sustainable movement is a strategy of using economic and human activities to support the environment and improve the quality of life. It involves discussing solutions to the many complex problems shared by communities across the globe—pollution, congestion, depletion of open space, inefficient energy consumption, and loss of a sense of place. Sustainable strategies are also about making systematic efforts to achieve a balanced, self-renewing environment. Sometimes this requires changing the way we understand geographic resources as well as approach their use and development. The examples in this book demonstrate how geographic knowledge can be applied to communities for monitoring natural areas, planning sensible urban developments, or observing human trends.

The notion of sustainable living offers hope for a better world. The *ESRI Map Book* acknowledges the important and impressive efforts of geographic information system (GIS) users who are collectively working to realize this vision. I particularly enjoy these efforts because they graphically demonstrate how to communicate complex problems and solutions in simple ways that are quickly understood. The stories that are illustrated show how geographic information helps support sustainable practices that preserve ecosystems, create safer neighborhoods, and provide more efficient infrastructure. They are a kind of geospatial language.

I believe these activities will make a difference in the evolution of our world.

Warm regards,

Jack Dangermond

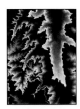

16 Mapping Kenya's Wildlands

18 Relative Wildness: A Look at the Condition of the Land

19 The Marjorie Harris Carr Cross Florida Greenway

20 GIS in the Public Interest

21 Cumberlands and Southern Ridge and Valley Ecoregion—Ecological Land Units

22 The Human Footprint and the Last of the Wild

23 Marine Ecoregional Planning at The Nature Conservancy—Running the SITES Algorithm to Construct a Marine Conservation Portfolio

24 Mesoamerican Trails—Preliminary Vision for a Trail Network

25 Vilcabamba–Amboro Conservation Megacorridor—Current Status

26 From the Forest to the Sea—Biodiversity Connections from Guinea to Togo

Education

27 Mount Desert Island Land Protection and Ownership

28 GIS in School Enrollment Forecasting—An Example for Bend, Oregon

29 Does the United States Need More Natural Disasters?

Environmental Management

30 Cumulative Effects Assessment (CEA)—Disturbance Mapping

31 Landscape Structure and Estuarine Condition in the Mid-Atlantic and Southern New England Region of the United States

32 Defining Environmental Corridors in Verona Township, Wisconsin, Using ModelBuilder

33 Marine Groundwater Map Series

34 Cedar River Municipal Watershed Road Deconstruction

35 Assessing and Remediation of the Environmental Damage at a Former Copper Mine Site

36 Using GIS to Examine the Effect of Scale in Assessing the Relationship Between Land Use and Stream Condition

37 Assessing Environmental Justice

38 Utility Infrastructure—Camp Pendleton

Government

Law Enforcement

39 Colorado Springs Police Department—Shots Fired

40 Salem/Keizer Sex Offenders—Schools and Child Care Centers with 1,000-Foot Buffer Zones

41 City of Salem, Oregon, Major Crime Incidents Report for April 2001

42 Washington, D.C.—Violent Crime Calls for Service

Business

4 San Francisco Bay Area—Estimated Ground Shaking

5 Retail Bank Branch Network Optimization

6 Residential Status and Consumer Behavior in Helsinki

7 Business Case Development

Cartography

8 USGS Maps-On-Line: Interactive Maps for the Greater San Francisco Bay Area

9 Crater Lake Revealed—Using GIS to Visualize and Analyze the Depths of Crater Lake, Oregon

10 The Well Locations for Riyadh City and Renew Old Maps

11 IFSAR DEM Merged with USGS DRG Morrison Quadrangle, Colorado

12 3D Visualization of Standard Topographical Maps Using GIS Vector Database Topo25

13 Guide to North American Meteorites

Conservation

14 Existing Conservation Network and California Wild Heritage Campaign

15 Sierra Nevada Forest Plan Amendment Project—Preferred Alternative Management Prescriptions

Public Safety

43 Tornado Damage Risk Assessment Estimating the Impact of a Big Outbreak to the Dallas–Fort Worth Metroplex

44 First Unit—Three-Minute Travel Time

State and Local Government

45 Existing Residential Units 1760–2001, Wake County

46 The Kentucky Single Zone State Plane Coordinate System

47 Demarcation of Municipalities in South Africa for Elections 2000

48 Fairfax County Selected Employer Locations

49 Southwest Las Vegas Valley Cost Analysis—Basin Development Clark County

50 Future Land Use

51 Pleasant Valley Resource Management Map

52 City of Evanston Zoning

53 Topography of the Town of Castle Rock

54 Map of Lexington–Fayette County

55 Digital Reference Maps of Capital Prague

56 Dallas Central Appraisal District Maps

57 Four Ultimate Receiving Waters of Torrance Storm Drainage

58 Projecting Urban Growth Using SAM-IM

59 Central City Maintenance Area

60 Integrated Urban Development

61 Infrastructure Repairs in Slide-Sensitive Areas—Work Activity 407

62 Tasmania 1:25,000 Series–Leventhorpe

63 City of New Berlin Assessor's Map

64 Development Constraints—Interstate 495 Region

65 Cape Cod Development Time Series, 1951–1999

66 Library Patron Density in San Joaquin County

Health and Human Services

67 Elementary School Performance and Social Service Benefit Recipients in Contra Costa County

68 The Changing Demography of the United States Racial Group with the Greatest Proportionate Increase in Total County Population, 1990–2000

69 The First Look at Census 2000

70 Africa: Applying GIS to the AIDS Pandemic

71 Community Service Maps

Natural Resources

Agriculture

72 Ecologically Valuated Soil Units—Digital Cadastral Maps

73 Cumberland County Farmland Preservation Program—Criteria for Evaluation

74 Remote Sensing and GIS in Soil Erosion Modeling

Forestry

75 Yukon Territory Maps

76 Sea-to-Sky Land and Resource Management Planning

77 Visual Impact Assessment

Mining and Earth Sciences

78 Geologic Map of Colorado National Monument and Adjacent Areas, Mesa County, Colorado

79 Geologic Map of the Ennis Quadrangle

80 Liquifaction Susceptibility Mapping, Ventura County, California

81 The Geological Map of Poland, Sheet Ozarow (819)

82 The Difference in Groundwater Between October 1990 and October 1993

83 Flooding of Underground Uranium Mine Workings

84 Fracture Density and Direction with Well Location Correlation Analysis

85 Bedrock Geology, Yukon Territory

86 GIS in Forest Administration of the Federation and the States of the Federal Republic of Germany

87 Seismic Hazard Maps for Southwest Asia

88 WV173 Monongahela Basin Mine Pool Project

89 Geological Map of Greece

90 Surficial Geology—Koroc River

Water

91 New Tools for Creating Common Understanding

92 Lake Whatcom, Bathymetric Map

93 Hydrogeologic Framework of Basin-Fill Aquifers in the Southwestern New Mexico Region—Integrating Framework Components Using GIS

94 Digital Bathymetric Model of Mono Lake, California

95 Analyzing Irrigated Land in Corrales, New Mexico

96 Water Source and Distribution Infrastructure in the Coal Slurry Spill Area of Concern

Sustainable Development

97 West Oakland Residential Development Assessment Model

98 Africa Water Balance

99 Africa Food Balance

100 Potential Build-Out Scenarios—Amherst, Massachusetts

101 Population Change in Baltic Sea Region Cities with More Than 10,000 Inhabitants, 1990s

Telecommunications

102 Commonwealth of Pennsylvania Radio Project System and Status

Tourism

103 Island Map—Hachijojima, Izu, Ogasawara (Bonin) Islands

104 Nevada Winnemucca Recreation Guide

105 Canadian Mountain Holidays—Hiking, Mountaineering, and Skiing

106 Santorini (Thira) Island, Aegean Islands, Greece

Transportation

107 Utah Valley Bike, Walk, and Bus Guide

108 Great Sandy Straight (South) Boating Safety Chart

109 General Highway Map, Barnes County

110 McCarran International Airport

111 Bikeways

112 California State Highway Map

113 Gwinnett County Transportation Plan

114 Harbor Loop Ferry

115 Population Growth and Employment Growth

116 Phase 1—Public Involvement

Utilities

Electric and Gas

117 Major Transmission Systems in New Mexico

118 Blackout Notifications

Water/Wastewater

119 Sweetwater Authority's Fire Hydrant Maintenance Program

120 Buffalo Sewer Authority

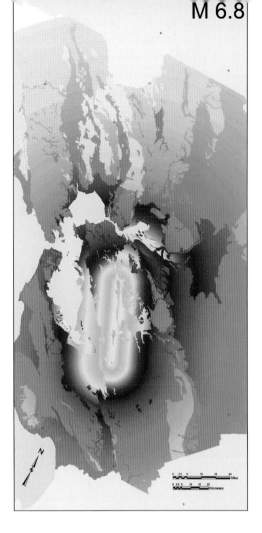

M 7.5

M 7.2

M 6.8

San Francisco Bay Area—Estimated Ground Shaking

Charles Schwab and Co., Inc

Hayward, California, USA

By Brian Quinn

Contact
Brian Quinn, bbq@craiova.com

Software
ArcInfo™ 8, ArcView® 3.2, ArcView Spatial Analyst, FEMA HAZUS, and Windows NT 4.0

Hardware
Pentium 800

Printer
HP DesignJet 1055CM

Data Source(s)
U.S. Geological Survey, California Geological Survey, Federal Emergency Management Agency, HAZUS numerical modeling

These maps visualize ground motion for three scenario earthquake events in a 14-county study region around the San Francisco Bay area. Ground motion estimates were calculated on a 200-meter grid using Federal Emergency Management Agency (FEMA) HAZUS 99. Amplification effects of geologic materials are from California Geological Survey's Vs-30 statewide 1:250,000 coverage. A thermal color ramp on 1-Hz spectral velocity conveys patterns of regional shaking to business process contingency planners. Losses are estimated in mid-1990's values.

The left panel is a moment magnitude M7.5 event to approximate the 1906 San Francisco earthquake, rupturing only from Tomales Bay to Cupertino. HAZUS estimated 1,050 deaths, 55 debris megatons, and $50 billion building and $25 billion business interruption losses.

The middle is an M7.2 event on the Hayward Fault–Rodgers Creek Fault system, rupturing from San Lorenzo to Petaluma. HAZUS estimated 720 deaths, 42 debris megatons, and $39 billion building and $18 billion business interruption losses.

The right panel is an M6.8 along Calaveras Fault from Calaveras Reservoir to Walnut Creek. HAZUS estimated 115 deaths, 32 debris megatons, and $15 billion building and $4 billion business interruption losses.

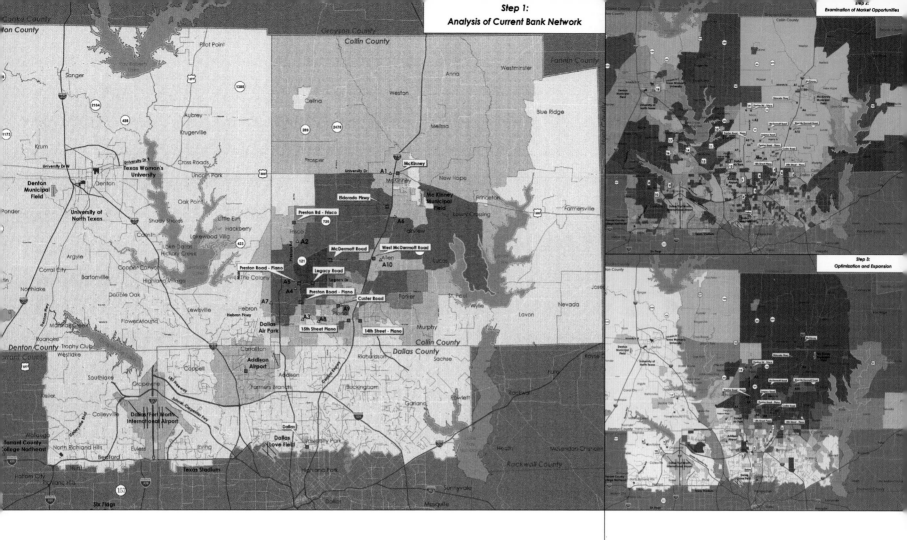

Step 1:
Analysis of Current Bank Network

Step 2:
Examination of Market Opportunities

Step 3:
Optimization and Expansion

This map presents a brief summary of the market analysis process employed by Verdi and Company, citing an example of a community bank in Plano, Texas. The process incorporates data from demographic vendors as well as proprietary data contained in the client's customer information files. Using these layers of information enables Verdi and Company to evaluate the institution's effectiveness of adequately servicing its customers and highlight those areas that may warrant new branch locations.

Verdi and Company's GIS division completes a comprehensive analysis of the market area under study. This includes analyzing total current population, projected population growth, current households, projected household growth, shifts in the population during the workday, and the location of retail shopping centers and plazas. In addition to standard market demographic characteristics, Verdi and Company analyzes the financial product potential held by the residential or consumer households in the market to determine the potential value of the market to a financial institution and incorporates an analysis of the client's customer accounts file or CIS. This analysis has enormous value to clients because they are not accustomed to thinking about the location or distribution of their customers in a geographic context. The visual presentation of this data for clients enables them to understand their present condition and see the areas where they may need to either improve their performance or add a new facility to capture areas of growth and high potential value.

This bank's network was found to cover its customers well, and Verdi and Company recommended new locations to expand its presence in the market. Presenting the institution's CIS in a thematic map format permitted management to think about its customers and network locations in a new way and spawned interesting discussions.

Retail Bank Branch Network Optimization
Verdi and Company
Buffalo, New York, USA
By Michael Bastedo

Contact
Michael Bastedo, michaelb@verdico.com

Software
ArcView 3.2 and Windows 2000

Hardware
Dell Precision 220 workstation

Printer
HP DesignJet 750C

Data Source(s)
Claritas and customer data

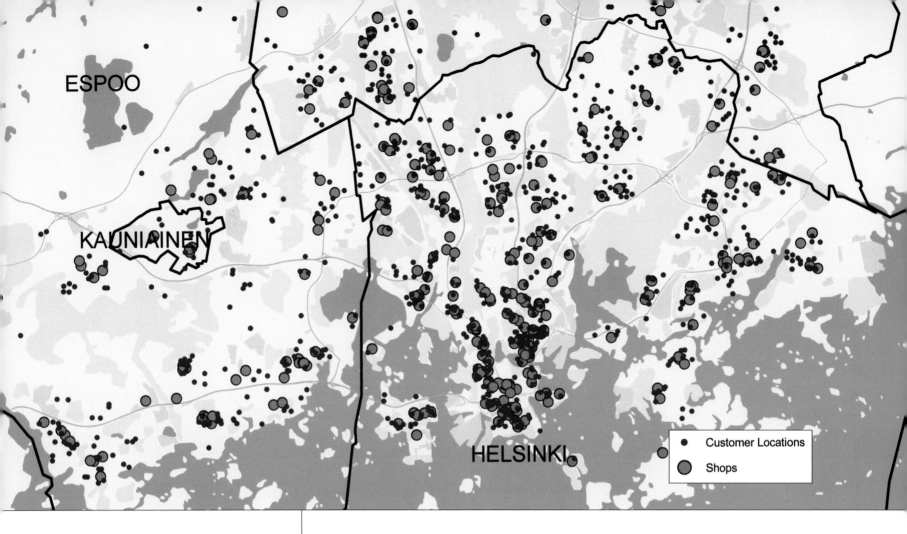

Customer Locations
Shops

Residential Status and Consumer Behavior in Helsinki

Helsinki School of Economics and Business Administration

Helsinki, Finland

By Antti Lehtinen and Jorma Pietala

Contact

Antti Lehtinen, antti.lehtinen@hkkk.fi

Software

ArcInfo 8.0.2, ArcView 3.2, ArcView Spatial Analyst, ArcView 3D Analyst™, SPSS 9, and Windows 2000

Printer

Epson Stylus Color 1520

Data Source(s)

AC Nielsen Finland and Statistics Finland

This map image is part of a larger series of study maps created to give an overview of the basic structure of grocery shops and to visualize outcomes of the different models used to analyze the interaction between shops and customers in the Helsinki metropolitan area.

Defining differentiated residential areas or area profiles finds distinctive customer segments for marketing and adjusts the supply to correspond to relevant demand. Target marketing can achieve better cost-efficiency, and the retail trade can increase efficiency in logistics and space management. This study sought to define differentiated residential areas indicated by a grid based on multivariate analysis and to identify the retail system by turnover and floor area. The interaction between shops and customers is analyzed by a multilinear model, which tries to give an overall picture of the performance of the retail system giving an individual attractiveness factor for supply units and a friction factor for customers.

A probabilistic model describes the behavior of the customers. The collection of all factor values defines probabilities for customers to visit any of the shops, and the model can be customized so that the likelihood of the observed pattern of shop visits is maximized by these probability values. The present model is fitted to a complete georeferenced customer–shop matrix, connecting all customers to all shops covered in the study. No functional form of the dependence of shopping probability on distance is postulated. Instead, the dependence is obtained from the model in numerical form. Any influence by a preconception of the researchers is kept at a minimum, and the data itself is allowed to determine the form of the distance law. Separate linear regression models have tested the resulting parameters. It showed that the shop-dependent parameter could accurately predict the turnover of a shop without any other information. If a new independent variable, the floor area, is added, the degree of explanation perked up from 61 to 82 percent.

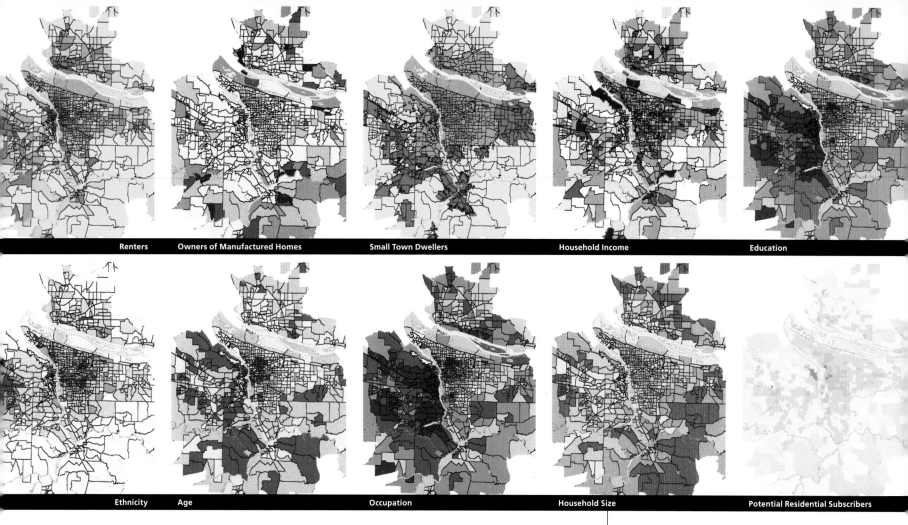

Renters   Owners of Manufactured Homes   Small Town Dwellers   Household Income   Education

Ethnicity   Age   Occupation   Household Size   Potential Residential Subscribers

Portland General Broadband (PGB), an affiliated company of Portland General Electric, plans to deploy approximately 104 miles of fiber in the Portland, Oregon, metropolitan area. To support the company's business plan and financial model, CH2M HILL conducted a GIS-based market analysis to evaluate market opportunity for various broadband services and estimate the number of potential residential and business subscribers. This information assisted PGB in network planning and design.

Business Case Development
CH2M HILL

Englewood, Colorado, USA

By Daniel Moreno

Contact
Daniel Moreno, dmoreno@ch2m.com

Software
ArcInfo and ArcView

Hardware
Compaq NT workstation

Printer
HP DesignJet 755

Data Source(s)
Various

USGS Maps-On-Line: Interactive Maps for the Greater San Francisco Bay Area

Telemorphic, Inc.

Berkeley, California, USA

By Todd Helt and Andrew Waxman, Telemorphic, Inc.; and Robert Lugo, U.S. Geological Survey (USGS)

Contact
Todd Helt, toddh@telemorphic.com

Software
ArcIMS®, MapImager Pro, Maplicity, and Windows 2000

Printer
HP DesignJet 3500C

Data Source(s)
USGS and Telemorphic, Inc.

The unique multiresolution, multisource image composite represents the various geospatial content currently available for the greater San Francisco Bay Area via the U.S. Geological Survey (USGS) Maps-On-Line Web site mapsonline.wr.usgs.gov. The USGS Western Geographic Science Center built Maps-On-Line using USGS baseline seamless geospatial data sets, Telemorphic's Java-based Maplicity viewer product, and ESRI's ArcIMS Internet GIS foundation. These tools enabled USGS to successfully implement the first public access Internet mapping site that provides Web browser-based users with real-time, interactive online image visualization and analysis tools.

With Maps-On-Line, USGS is able to deliver not only the GIS data but also the image processing and GIS tools required to make use of the data. Such broad, Web browser-based accessibility introduces geospatial technologies to a larger audience via the Internet.

Telemorphic, Inc., created the geographic image composite seen in the main map area using MapImager Pro, the company's image processing software. The Landsat 7 satellite image incrementally blends with high-resolution shaded relief data moving from west to east until the Landsat data becomes completely transparent. Simultaneously, USGS digital raster graphics are clearly visible in the central portion of the map area and then gradually fade moving from the center outward to the edges of the map.

50-Meter Isobaths

Geologic Map

Approximately 500,000 people visit Crater Lake National Park each year. Located in the Cascade range of southern Oregon, the area's volcanic peaks, evergreen forests, and the lake's blue water are the park's main attractions. Crater Lake partially fills the caldera that formed approximately 7,700 years ago by the eruption and subsequent collapse of a 12,000-foot volcano called Mt. Mazama. The caldera-forming or climactic eruption of Mt. Mazama drastically changed the landscape and spread a blanket of volcanic ash as far away as southern Canada.

Mt. Mazama had a 400,000-year history of activity similar to Mt. Shasta and other Cascade volcanic centers. Since the climactic eruption, there have been several less violent, smaller postcaldera eruptions within the caldera. Relatively little was known about these events as their products were obscured beneath Crater Lake's surface. Because the Crater Lake region is still potentially volcanically active, understanding past eruptive events could be important to understanding future eruptions, which could threaten facilities and people at the park and a major transportation corridor east of the Cascades.

The lake bottom was mapped with a high-resolution multibeam echo sounder. The new bathymetric survey provides a two-meter per pixel view of the lake floor from its deepest basins virtually to the shoreline. GIS applications enable the bathymetry data to be visualized and analyzed, which will shed some light on the geology, geomorphology, and geologic history of Crater Lake. The new bathymetric data along with detailed geologic mapping and images and samples from a manned submersible, sediment cores, and dredged rocks has yielded a geologic map of the lake bottom, a history of lake filling, and determinations of volumes, times, and rates of postcaldera eruptions. These calculations have been useful in assembling a geologic history for Crater Lake from the time of caldera formation to present day.

Crater Lake Revealed—Using GIS to Visualize and Analyze the Depths of Crater Lake, Oregon

U.S. Geological Survey (USGS), University of New Hampshire, and U.S. Department of Interior, National Park Service

Menlo Park, California, USA

By Charles R. Bacon, Mark W. Buketenica, Peter Dartnell, James V. Gardner, Larry A. Mayer, Manuel Nathenson, David W. Ramsey, and Joel E. Robinson

Contact
David Ramsey, dramsey@usgs.gov

Software
ArcInfo 7.2.1, ArcGrid™, ArcView 3.2, ArcView 3D Analyst, and ArcView Spatial Analyst, UNIX, and Windows NT

Hardware
Sun Ultra Enterprise 4000 workstation and SGI workstation

Printer
HP DesignJet 2500CP

Data Source(s)
USGS

The Well Locations for Riyadh City

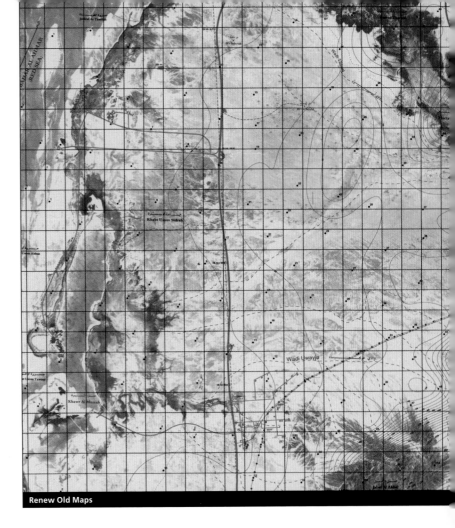

Renew Old Maps

The Well Locations for Riyadh City and Renew Old Maps

King Abdul Aziz City for Science and Technology

Riyadh, Saudi Arabia

By Khaled Al-Ahmadi and Rami Nawasrah

Contact
Khaled Al-Ahmadi, kalahmadi_sa@hotmail.com

Software
ArcGIS™, ArcInfo 8.1, ArcView 3D Analyst, ArcView Spatial Analyst, ERDAS IMAGINE, Microsoft Access, and Windows NT

Hardware
Compaq workstation

Printer
HP DesignJet 2500CP and HP DesignJet 5000CP

Data Source(s)
Saudi Center for Remote Sensing, SPOT, IKONOS, and IRS satellite images; Ministry of Petroleum and Mineral Resources; Ministry of Agriculture and Water; and Ministry of Transportation

The Well Locations for Riyadh City

These maps of the wells in Riyadh, Saudi Arabia, were created for the Ministry of Agriculture and Water (MAW). The MAW compiled a spatial database from field surveys using a global positioning system (GPS) and an Access database with descriptive information about all the wells in Riyadh. Linking the databases along with satellite imagery of the area to a GIS enables the MAW to accurately locate wells and retrieve up-to-date information about them.

Researchers at the MAW use these maps, which can be printed at various scales, to monitor historical information about the wells, assess future water needs, and plan for new wells.

Renew Old Maps

This map was part of a series produced to replace maps from the Ministry of Petroleum that were made in 1975. The old paper maps were scanned; the data was converted from raster to vector and combined with satellite imagery. King Abdul Aziz City for Science and Technology provided a triangulated irregular network coverage and added contours to the areas.

3D Surface Model

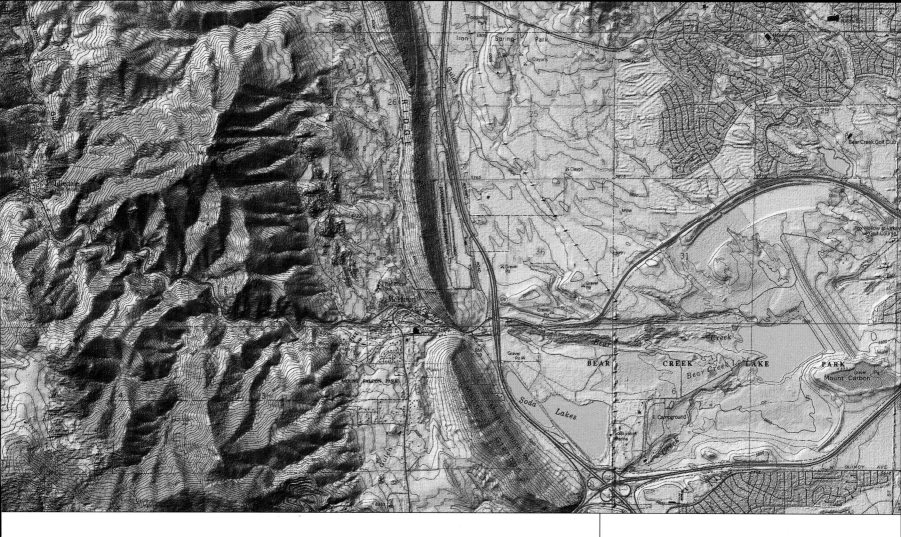

Technological advances have enabled increased accuracies, higher resolutions, and reduced costs for elevation data acquired using airborne Interferometric Synthetic Aperture Radar (IFSAR) and Light Detection and Ranging (LIDAR) technologies. The U.S. Geological Survey (USGS) acquired IFSAR coverage for the Colorado Front Range area and is evaluating both IFSAR and LIDAR for its Elevation program.

A hillshade grid, created from the reflective-surface IFSAR digital elevation model (DEM), was fused with the USGS digital raster graphic (DRG) for the Morrison quadrangle to illustrate both the horizontal agreement between the two disparate data types and the potential for using such a merged data set in map feature revision and graphic product generation.

The IFSAR DEM, which contained over-edge coverage outside the quadrangle neatlines, was reprojected from UTM NAD 83 to UTM NAD 27 and clipped to the neatline to match the datum and extent of the DRG. An ARC Macro Language (AML™) program was written to create a hillshade grid from the elevation source, resample the hillshade to match the native DRG cell size, and merge the hillshade and DRG grids. The original DRG color saturation was maintained rather than blended with the elevation gray tones.

IFSAR DEM Merged with USGS DRG
Morrison Quadrangle, Colorado
U.S. Geological Survey (USGS)

Denver, Colorado, USA

By John Kosovich and John List

Contact
John Kosovich, jjkosovich@usgs.gov

Software
ArcInfo 8.0.2, ArcPress™, UNIX, and Windows NT

Hardware
SGI 320 and SGI server

Printer
HP DesignJet 2000

Data Source(s)
Intermap Technologies, Inc., and USGS

3D Visualization of Standard Topographical Maps Using GIS Vector Database Topo25
General Command of Mapping

Ankara, Turkey

By H. Hakan Maras and Mehmet Ustun

Contact
H. Hakan Maras, hmaras@hgk.mil.tr

Software
ArcInfo 7.2.1 and Windows

Hardware
Pentium III

Printer
HP DesignJet 750C

Data Source(s)
Topo25 vector data

Perception of the third dimension on topographical maps, in which the height information is represented with contours, is very difficult and requires experience. These three-dimensional maps reflect the shape of terrain in one quick look while providing a range of uses such as civil engineering, military operations, and transportation planning.

Another important aspect of the maps is that you do not need any special glasses, which disturb the shape of terrain. All the details are put on the relief of the terrain, which helps with accurate decision making. In both models, the contour (elevation) coverage is converted to a triangulated irregular network from which a lattice was produced. The colored map was created using a hue-saturation-value grid model. The black-and-white map was produced via the hillshade function.

General Command of Mapping

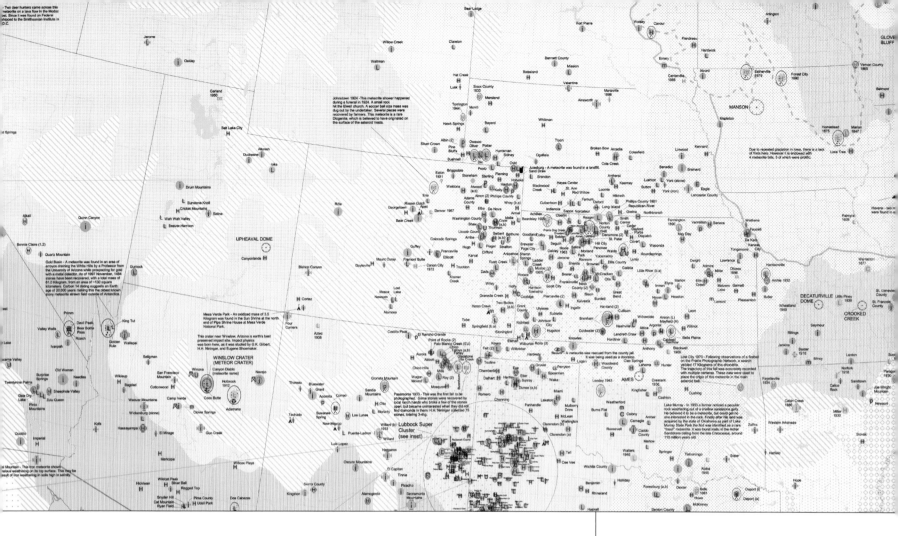

The Guide to North American Meteorites is a wall map featuring more than 1,250 meteorite and crater occurrences. Each meteorite displays name, mass, class, and other features such as strewn fields. The year is printed for each witnessed fall. Craters are depicted as well, and those larger than 20 kilometers are shown to scale. The coverage includes the continental United States, Mexico, and part of Canada. Twenty-six of the meteorites are annotated describing specific circumstances of general interest. The data plotted on the Guide to North American Meteorites includes those meteorites published in the *British Museum's Catalogue of Meteorites,* 4th edition (1985), and subsequent issues of the *Meteoritical Bulletin.* Published meteorite locations were checked using a GIS, and the reported county for each meteorite was checked against the county in which it was plotted. Some corrections were made, and error bars are indicated on uncertain locations.

Fifteen meteorite classes are coded using letters of the English alphabet, and mass recovered is coded using different sized circles. Falls are indicated with a red circle, and finds are shown in blue. This color coding brings out a striking pattern of meteorite finds on the high plains of Texas, New Mexico, Kansas, and Colorado.

Ecoregions are shaded. Meteorite find locations have some correlation with ecoregions, and a bimodal distribution was discovered between iron and stony meteorites. Stony meteorite finds are highly concentrated on the Great Plains in the steppe ecoregion. This elevated, flat, and dry region is favorable for meteorite preservation and exposure. However, iron meteorite finds are slightly deficient on the Great Plains when compared with wet areas such as the Appalachian Mountains. For more information on each of these meteorites or to purchase the meteorite map, go to www.meteoritemaps.com.

Guide to North American Meteorites
Philmont

Cimarron, New Mexico, USA

By Bill Peck

Contact
Bill Peck, bpeck@meteoritemaps.com

Software
ArcView 3.2 and Windows NT 4.0

Hardware
Dell

Printer
HP DesignJet 1055CM

Data Source(s)
Various publications and University of Wyoming

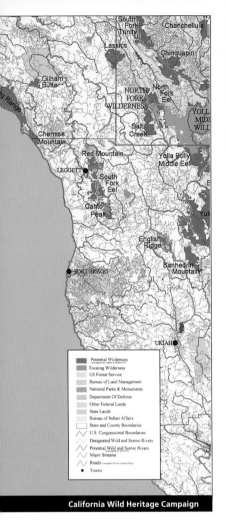

California Wild Heritage Campaign

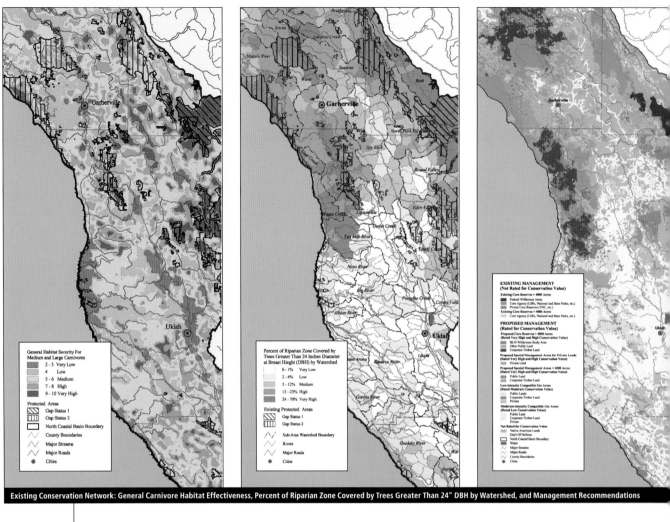

Existing Conservation Network: General Carnivore Habitat Effectiveness, Percent of Riparian Zone Covered by Trees Greater Than 24" DBH by Watershed, and Management Recommendations

Existing Conservation Network and California Wild Heritage Campaign

Legacy—The Landscape Connection

Arcata, California, USA

By Curtice Jacoby and Chris Trudel

Contact
Curtice Jacoby, jacoby@legacy-tlc.org

Software
ArcInfo and ArcView

Hardware
HP Kayak XU

Printer
HP DesignJet 750C+ (Existing Conservation Network) and HP DeskJet 1220C (California Wild Heritage Campaign)

Data Source(s)
California Department of Fish and Game, California Natural Diversity Database, U.S. Geological Survey, California Gap Analysis, California Heritage Campaign Potential, Sierra Biodiversity Institute, U.S. Forest Service, ESRI, and Legacy—The Landscape Connection

California Wild Heritage Campaign—Potential Wilderness and Wild Rivers

Potential wilderness areas that are crucial to Legacy's conservation vision for the California North Coast are the relatively undisturbed areas without roads that serve as corridors and stepping-stones for wildlife moving between the large areas of officially protected wilderness. Working with the California Wild Heritage Campaign, Legacy transferred field maps into ArcInfo coverages that were used to calculate acres and distances accurately. Legacy coordinated an intensive GIS program that involved coordinating 15 people from seven organizations across California. Boundaries were digitized for 230 potential wilderness areas totaling 7,271,055 acres. This map of potential wilderness and wild rivers focuses on northwestern California.

Existing Conservation Network

Logging, mining, road and dam building, and other forms of development threaten the continued existence of intact ecosystems and the ecosystem services that they supply. Sensitive fish, wildlife, and other native biodiversity are becoming increasingly rare. The relatively few acres of publicly owned or otherwise protected lands in the region are not enough to fully protect the ecological integrity of the North Coast region of northwestern California.

Four types of conservation methods are important in stemming the tide of extinction—land purchase, conservation easements, designation of public land as wilderness, and increased enforcement of existing laws. Legacy has assessed the relative conservation values of lands in the region to help prioritize the implementation of these different conservation methods. The Management Recommendations for the North Coast Region map shows possible changes in management based on ownership and conservation value.

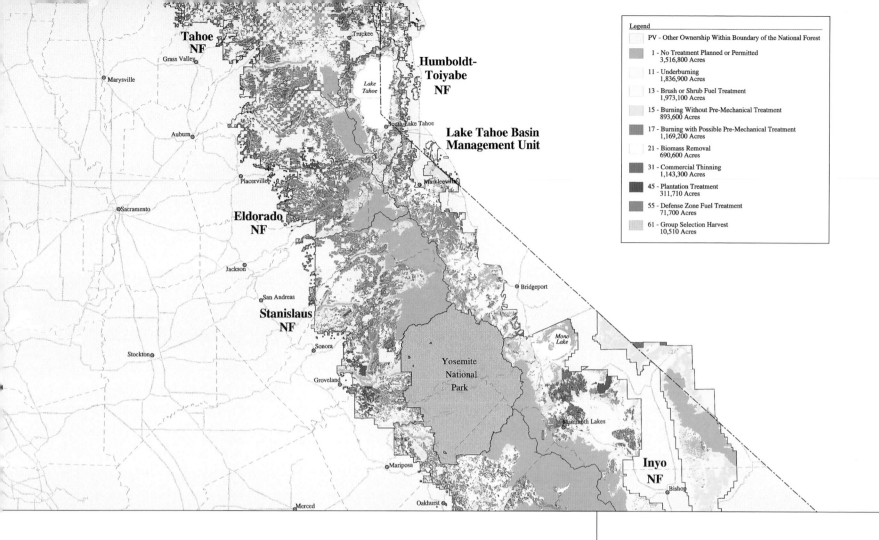

The Sierra Nevada Forest Plan Amendment Final Environmental Impact Statement presents nine different alternatives for stewardship of 11 national forests in the Sierra Nevada Range and Modoc Plateau. These alternatives aim to sustain the old forest ecosystem; protect and restore aquatic, riparian, and meadow ecosystems; improve fire and fuel management; combat noxious weeds; and sustain lower west side hardwood ecosystems. The alternatives describe different possibilities for amending the land and resource management plans for the Modoc, Lassen, Plumas, Tahoe, Eldorado, Stanislaus, Sequoia, Sierra, and Inyo National Forests; the Lake Tahoe Basin Management Unit; and portions of the Humboldt–Toiyabe National Forest in the Sierra Nevada range.

The theme of the Preferred Alternative is to manage sensitive wildlife habitat cautiously. It seeks to provide for species conservation while addressing the need to reduce the threat of fire to human communities.

Uncertainty about the possible effects of management activities on wildlife habitat is a dominant concern. Management direction is designed to address this uncertainty and increase confidence that management actions will not adversely affect wildlife habitat. In addition, the Preferred Alternative provides more spatially explicit California spotted owl and fish conservation strategies and better integration of these strategies with its aquatic management and fire and fuels management strategies.

Vegetation treatments are limited to those designed for fire hazard reduction, maintenance activities, or public health and safety. This alternative also prescribes more intensive fuel treatments in urban/wildland intermix zones. Outside these zones, the direction for treating forest fuels is more conservative, which reduces the potential for treatments to degrade habitat.

Sierra Nevada Forest Plan Amendment Project—Preferred Alternative Management Prescriptions

U.S. Department of Agriculture (USDA) Forest Service

Sacramento, California, USA

By Tim Lindemann and Kurt Teuber

Contact
Kurt Teuber, kteuber@fs.fed.us

Software
ArcInfo 7.2.1 and UNIX

Hardware
IBM AIX

Printer
HP DesignJet 1055CM

Data Source(s)
USDA Forest Service

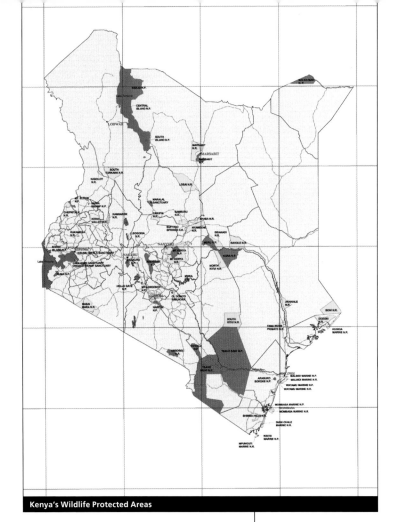

Kenya's Wildlife Protected Areas

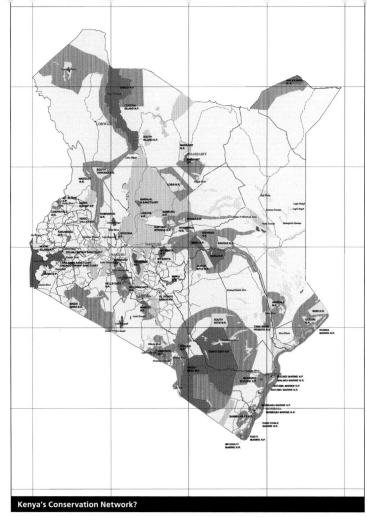

Kenya's Conservation Network?

Mapping Kenya's Wildlands

Kenya Wildlife Service (KWS)

Nairobi, Kenya

By Rose Mayienda, W.K. Mutero, T. Muthui, and G. Tokro *(Wildlife Protected Areas)*

Rose Mayienda, W.K. Mutero, and G. Tokro *(Conservation Network)*

Contact
Wycliffe Mutero, muterow@kws.org

Software
ArcView and Windows 95

Hardware
Compaq and Dell

Printer
HP DesignJet 750C+

Data Source(s)
KWS and Survey of Kenya

Kenya's Wildlife Protected Areas

Kenya's wildlife protected area system consists of parks, reserves, and sanctuaries. The approximate area of Kenya's wildlife protected area system is 47,674 square kilometers. This is approximately 8.2 percent of Kenya's land area and includes a few reserves that are proposed but not official. Kenya Wildlife Service (KWS) is working with its partners to expand the current existing wildlife protected area system through the creation of community and private conservation areas.

Kenya's Conservation Network?

Human population pressure on Kenya's wildlife protected system continues to mount, leading to the question of whether there is a minimum viable conservation area for Kenya. The assumption is that below this minimum area, the biodiversity within the various conservation areas will spiral downward and ultimately become extinct. This map is a rough draft that attempts to capture Kenya's minimum conservation area network, which consists mainly of wildlife protected areas, wildlife dispersal areas, wildlife migration corridors, and other areas of biodiversity such as forests.

The conservation network depicted here goes outside the borders of the wildlife protected area system, of which KWS has jurisdiction. Because of this, KWS recognizes the great need to work with partners in areas outside its mandated area of operation. The hope is that with this strategy, conservation efforts in Kenya will become successful.

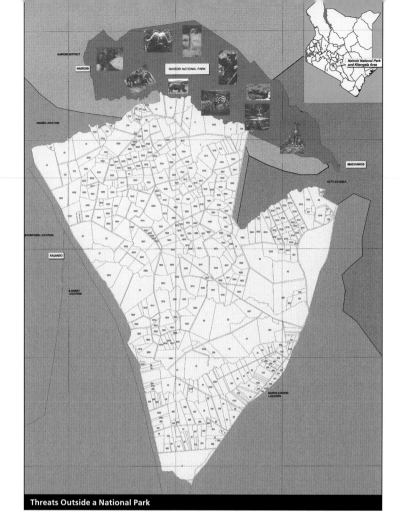

Threats Outside a National Park

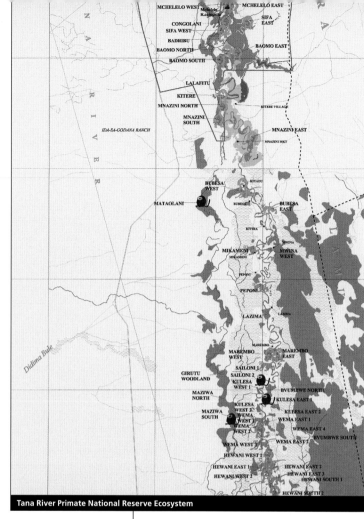

Tana River Primate National Reserve Ecosystem

Threats Outside a National Park

Nairobi National Park is under threat from human development activities. Of major concern is the potential impact of development to the south of the park, which can sever the vital link that connects this small park to a bigger and more viable ecosystem to its south. To counter the threat, park management together with the Friends of Nairobi National Park designed the Wildlife Conservation Lease Programme. Under the program, landowners of the adjudicated land shown in the map are provided with financial incentives. In return, they are expected to offer wildlife unrestricted access to their land and to adopt pro-wildlife measures such as leaving their land unfenced and undeveloped. After a modest start, the program is steadily gaining currency. This program's goal is to safeguard all the land that the wildlife in the park needs for dispersal and migration.

Tana River Primate National Reserve Ecosystem

The Tana River Primate National Reserve is part of the Tana River ecosystem, which extends spatially from the water catchment areas of Mt. Kenya to the Tana Delta. It is home to two critically endangered primates—the Tana River Red Colobus and the Tana River Crested Mangabey. The Kenya Wildlife Service is using GIS to inform management about these two important primates and the ecosystem they live in.

Mapping Kenya's Wildlands

Kenya Wildlife Service (KWS)

Nairobi, Kenya

By Rose Mayienda, W.K. Mutero, and G. Tokro *(Threats)*

Apollo Kariuki, Moses Maloba, and W.K. Mutero *(Tana)*

Contact
Wycliffe Mutero, muterow@kws.org

Software
ArcView and Windows 98

Hardware
Compaq and Dell

Printer
HP DesignJet 750C+

Data Source(s)
KWS, Survey of Kenya, and Kenya Department of Resource Surveys and Remote Sensing

Relative Wildness
A Look at the
Condition of the Land

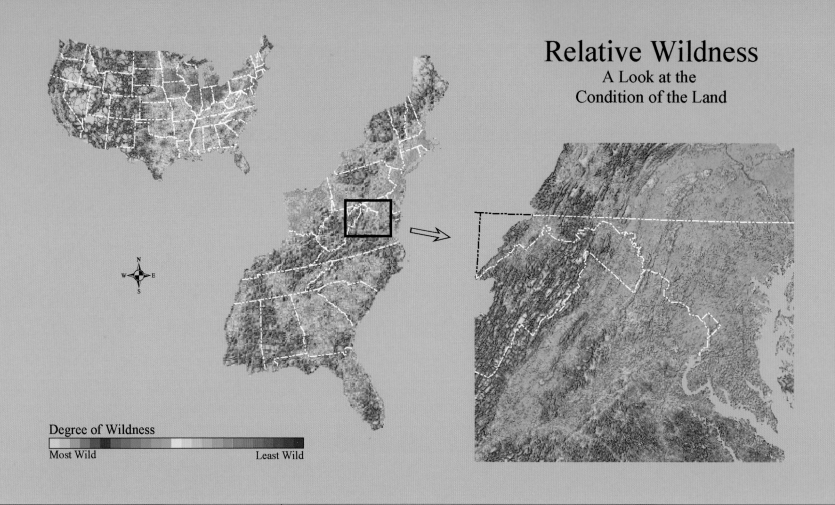

Degree of Wildness

Most Wild   Least Wild

Relative Wildness: A Look at the Condition of the Land
The Wilderness Society

Seattle, Washington, USA

By Greg Aplet and Mark Wilbert

Contact
Mark Wilbert, mwilbert@twsnw.org

Software
Arcinfo 8 and Windows NT 4.0

Printer
HP DesignJet 1055CM

Data Sources
U.S. Department of Transportation, U.S. Census Bureau, U.S. Army Corps of Engineers, U.S. Geological Survey, Defense Mapping Satellite Program, U.S. Environmental Protection Agency, Environmental Defense, National Geophysical Data Center, and ArcData℠

Wildness is an attribute of the land reflecting its naturalness and its freedom from human control. Wildness captures not only important elements of ecological integrity but aspects of the land relating to the human experience of a place such as its remoteness and its provision of solitude. The maps depict an "index of wildness" created by combining information representing this naturalness and freedom—population density, distance from roads, pollution and ecosystem composition, structure, and function.

Wildness is continuous. Within a given landscape all lands fall within the continuum of wildness that ranges from most wild to least wild for that landscape. Wildness is relative. In one landscape, an area may fall nearer one end of the wildness continuum, while in a larger or smaller landscape it may fall nearer the other end. For example, in the context of the contiguous United States, much of the Appalachian Mountains are only moderately wild, and even the largest city park receives the lowest wildness rating. In the context of the eastern United States, however, the Appalachians are some of the wildest lands, and in the context of a city, a large park also receives a high wildness rating.

Wildness mapping can help us visualize general land condition, corroborate the importance of lands already targeted for protection, and suggest areas where restoration work is needed. In conjunction with other information, wildness maps can help develop a robust plan for the protection of a network of wildlands stretching from the most intimate urban green spaces to our nation's largest wilderness areas.

The Marjorie Harris Carr Cross Florida Greenway is a unique conservation and recreation project passing through four Florida counties on lands formerly dedicated to the construction of a proposed cross-Florida barge canal. Traversing Citrus, Levy, Marion, and Putnam Counties, the greenway comprises a multitude of habitats and ecosystem types throughout its 110-mile extent. Florida's Department of Landscape Architecture is home to an interdisciplinary team charged with the development of a comprehensive plan for the management of the greenway. The planning team is using the latest technology and research to provide for ecological and historical restoration, the development of recreation opportunities, and the creation of interpretation programs to provide visitors with a clear understanding of the greenway's history and significance.

The first phase of the greenway's existence as a conservation and recreation corridor began with a management plan developed in 1992 at the University of Florida (UF). The scope of the original study was broad, ranging from an analysis of project boundaries to the formulation of restoration, conservation, recreation, and policy recommendations for the management of specific areas and the greenway.

In March of 2001, faculty and students in the Department of Landscape Architecture and Urban and Regional Planning at the UF began work on a new management plan for the greenway. This new plan, envisioned as a multidisciplinary, interdepartmental effort, will make use of GIS, data management, and Web design technology to provide a wealth of information. The planning team will create a pool of internal resources, both historical and current, that will be passed onto the Office of Greenways and Trails upon the completion of the project.

The Marjorie Harris Carr Cross
Florida Greenway
University of Florida, Department of Landscape Architecture, Cross Florida Greenway Management Plan Project

Gainesville, Florida, USA

By Christopher D. Stoll

Contact
Christopher D. Stoll, cstoll@ufl.edu

Software
ArcGIS 8.1, Adobe Photoshop 6.0, and Windows NT

Printer
HP DesignJet 750C

Data Source(s)
Florida Geographic Data Library

Assessing Development in Martis Valley, California

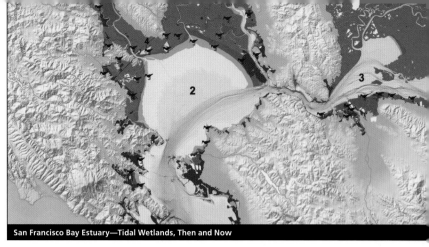
San Francisco Bay Estuary—Tidal Wetlands, Then and Now

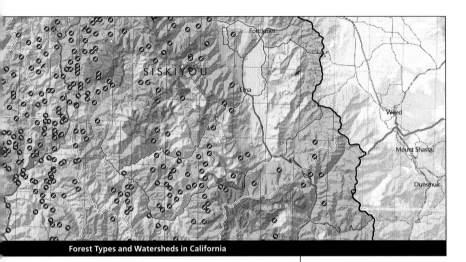
Forest Types and Watersheds in California

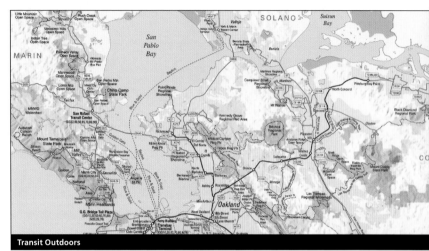
Transit Outdoors

GIS in the Public Interest

GreenInfo Network

Culver City and San Francisco, California, USA

By David Cameron, Brian Cohen, Louis Jaffe, and Peter Kostishack

Contact

Larry Orman, info@greeninfo.org

Software

ArcView 3.x, Adobe Illustrator/Photoshop, MAPublisher, and Windows NT

Printer

HP DesignJet 1055CM

Data Source(s)

U.S. Geological Survey; Nevada/Placer County and Truckee General Plans; EcoAtlas of San Francisco Estuary Institute; California Gap Analysis Program; Geographic Data Technology, Inc.; U.S. Environmental Protection Agency; California Department of Conservation; and Protected Open Space Database

Assessing Development in Martis Valley, California

Created for Sierra Watch, a citizen advocacy organization, this map portrays existing and planned development near Lake Tahoe. The map has helped the group focus on habitat and other impacts of proposed resort development. Cartographically, it is highly effective in using shaded relief to inform but not overpower the development information.

San Francisco Bay Estuary—Tidal Wetlands, Then and Now

This poster map was originally created as a centerfold for *Bay Nature* magazine. It depicts the San Francisco Bay Area as its landforms existed before settlement and shows the extent of wetlands filling and diking. The color scheme is intentionally rich, and the map shows the bathymetry of the San Francisco Bay—the first time this information has been mapped with the topography of the region forming a complete vision of the area.

Forest Types and Watersheds in California

Used to assist organization strategy planning by Environment Now, this poster shows major forest types in California in relation to watershed and jurisdictional data. The map seeks to balance relief with thematic data while providing legible detail in roads and other boundary data. It steps the viewer into the information rather than presenting it all at a level of first impression. At the same time, its detail enables close inspection.

Transit Outdoors

Prepared for *Bay Nature* magazine, this offset-produced map shows linkages between public open space and the San Francisco Bay Area bus and other transit systems. More than 60,000 copies were produced and distributed. The challenge was to create a very pale shaded relief to highlight the parks and transit connections. The original retains hill forms in the white areas and detailed information in the shadows of the parklands.

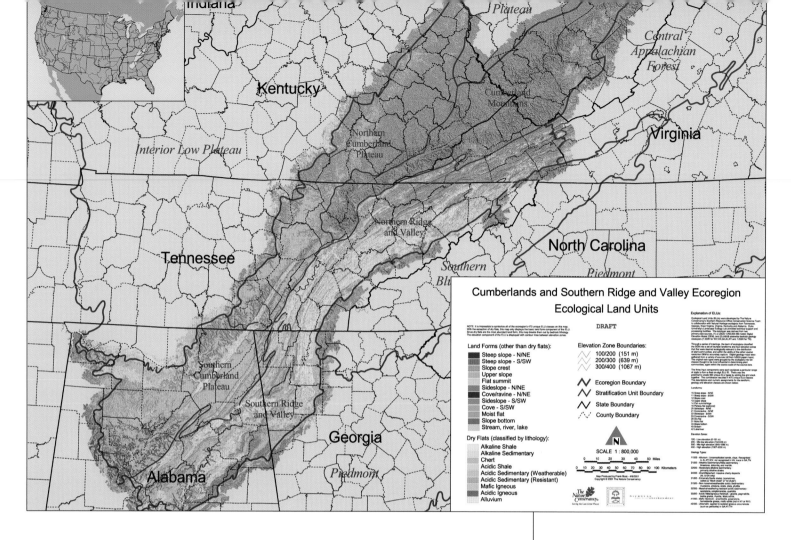

The Nature Conservancy's conservation process starts by designing portfolios of conservation areas within and across ecoregions. These ecoregional portfolios represent the full distribution and diversity of native species, natural communities, and ecological systems within each ecoregion. The Conservancy develops and uses ecological land units (ELUs) as a synthetic surrogate for biological information. ELUs express the stable underlying physical features that structure a site, and each one depicts a unique combination of three factors—geology, land form, and elevation zones. Largely, the distribution of the ELUs determines the types and distribution of biodiversity features across a landscape.

For this ecoregion, a team of ecologists classified the digital elevation model (DEM) into a set of 14 landforms and four elevation zones that was deemed ecologically relevant to the distribution of plant communities across the ecoregion. Ecologists grouped original rock types from digital geology maps into 11 classes thought to be most influential in determining plant communities, and three grids were each reclassified into a particular range of digits to form a final five-digit ELU. Added together, the combination resulted in 470 unique ELU classes, which were used to characterize and select potential conservation areas that would capture the full range of biophysical habitats in an ecoregional portfolio.

The ELU data layer is also used more generally to help predict vegetation distributions, delineate ecosystems, estimate biodiversity, and design stratified sampling schemes for field inventory and remote sensing projects. The ELU concept is scalable from sites to continents with appropriate changes to the character and resolution of the input variables.

Cumberlands and Southern Ridge and Valley Ecoregion—Ecological Land Units
The Nature Conservancy

Durham, North Carolina, USA

By Frank Biasi

Contact
Frank Biasi, fbiasi@tnc.org

Software
ArcInfo 7.2, ArcView 3.2, and Windows 2000

Printer
HP DesignJet 2500CP

Data Source(s)
U.S. Geological Survey and ESRI

The Human Footprint

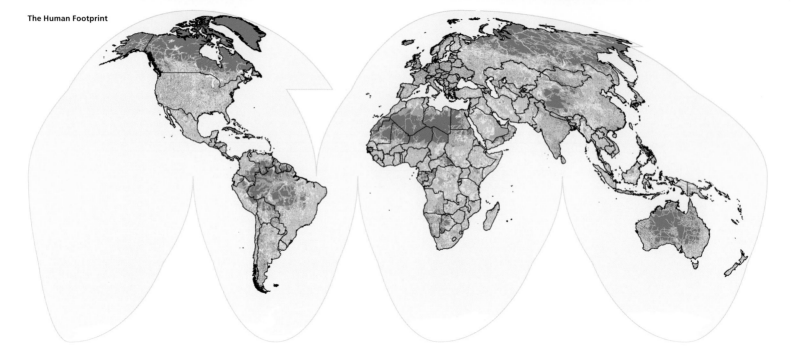

The Last of the Wild

Human Influence

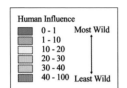

	0 - 1	Most Wild
	1 - 10	
	10 - 20	
	20 - 30	
	30 - 40	
	40 - 100	Least Wild

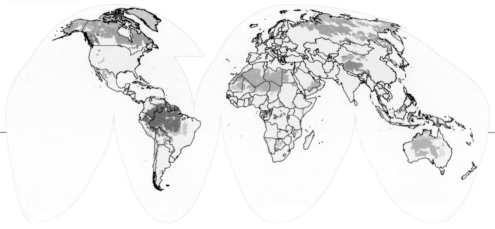

The Human Footprint
and the Last of the Wild

Wildlife Conservation Society and Center for
International Earth Science Information (CIESIN)

New York, New York, USA

By Malanding Jaiteh, Marc Levy, Kent H. Redford,
Eric W. Sanderson, Antoinette Wannebo,
and Gillian Woolmer

Contact

Eric W. Sanderson, esanderson@wcs.org

Software

ArcInfo 7.2.1, ArcView 3.2, Windows NT, and
Windows 2000

Printer

HP DesignJet 755CM

Data Source(s)

CIESIN, U.S. National Imagery and Mapping Agency,
Defense Meteorological Satellite Program, U.S.
Geological Survey, and World Wildlife Fund

The human footprint is everywhere, and the Human Footprint map is about visualizing the extent of this influence beyond our local neighborhoods. To see how human beings influence the planet on a global scale, a GIS team combined data from public databases on land use, settlements, power infrastructure, access from roads and rivers, and human population density to estimate the human footprint. According to the analysis, human beings directly impact 83 percent of the Earth's surface in one or more ways. Of the remaining uninfluenced areas, nearly all (88 percent) are confined to deserts or boreal and arctic regions where it is not possible to grow rice, wheat, or maize.

Mapping the human footprint also enables us to map its inverse—the last of the wild. Normalizing across biomes in major regions of the world, analysts sought out data on the largest, wildest places left on the land's surface (different colors on the map indicate different biomes). Conservation of these areas, which by definition have fewer people and less human use, may in the near term provide our best hope for conservation of wildlife and wilderness, particularly as human population and consumption continue to grow unabated.

Ultimately the question of the human footprint is—what will we do with our dominion on Earth? Many of us believe that we have a responsibility that accompanies our natural rights to protect the land and waters and all the creatures, large and small. Human beings are experts at modifying the environment to our own ends. What will we do with our expertise now?

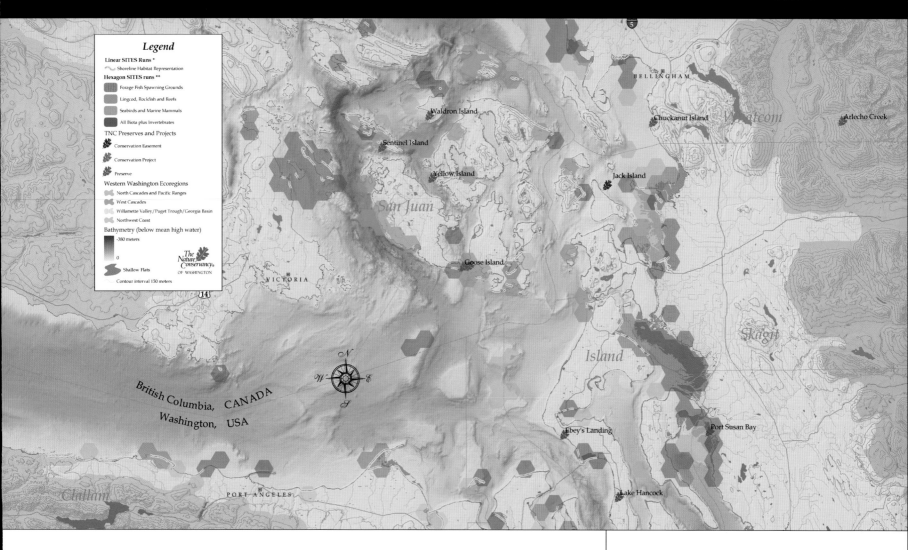

The Nature Conservancy of Washington is currently working on the Willamette Valley/Puget Trough/Georgia Basin ecoregion to identify marine and terrestrial areas that capture viable examples of native species and habitats. Ecoregional planning entails selecting sites from among a larger set of planning units within this ecoregion spanning the lowlands of western Oregon, Washington, and British Columbia. This collection of selected planning units, termed the "conservation portfolio," provides a systematic basis for site planning and acquisition.

Integrating the marine environment into the ecoregional planning process presents many challenges and opportunities. Traditionally, the organization has focused on biodiversity on land, but the shoreline and marine components make up a significant amount of the overall biodiversity of the region. Using a site selection algorithm called SITES (www.biogeog.ucsb.edu/projects/tnc/toolbox.html), data sets were collected for both shoreline habitats and species distributions in the nearshore area that attempt to best capture a marine conservation portfolio. The British Columbia, Canada, and Washington, USA, ShoreZone data sets were used for shoreline habitats to derive 39 representative shoreline types or more than 8,000 kilometers of continuous data. Data sets for 130 marine species and habitats were collected. The first credible iteration of this plan will focus on the nearshore environment down to 40 meters below mean high water, largely due to data quality. Two different spatial formats, linear segments and hexagons, were used as planning units. There are four hexagon scenarios represented on the map for different taxa groups. With each progressive scenario (from red to blue), planning units were "locked in" to the analysis to ensure site consistency. The results shown represent the first step in building the portfolio; hexagons and linear units guide the delineation of sites but will not be part of the final product.

The portfolio will reflect a combined approach that is both analytical (data-driven) and delphic (driven by expert review). The methodology is now being exported to other ecoregions within the Pacific Northwest Division of The Nature Conservancy.

Marine Ecoregional Planning at The Nature Conservancy—Running the SITES Algorithm to Construct a Marine Conservation Portfolio

The Nature Conservancy

Seattle, Washington, USA

By Zach Ferdaña

Contact

Zach Ferdaña, zferdana@tnc.org

Software

ArcMap™ and Windows 2000

Hardware

Dell 420 workstation

Printer

HP DesignJet 1055CM

Data Source(s)

Washington Department of Natural Resources, British Columbia Ministry of Sustainable Resource Management, Washington Department of Fish and Wildlife, The Nature Conservancy of Washington, and marine experts in British Columbia and Washington

The Nature Conservancy

RESULTADOS DE TALLERES NACIONALES
Results from National Workshops

RUTAS CONCEPTUALES
Conceptual Routes

PRINCIPAL/ Principal
FERROSENDERO/ Railtrail
NACIONAL/ National
SENDEROS EXISTENTES/ Existing Trails
CARRETERA ESCENICA/ Scenic Highway
CARRETERA PRINCIPAL/ Principal Highway
ACUATICA PRINCIPAL/ Principal Aquatic
ACUATICA NACIONAL/ National Aquatic

Mesoamerican Trails—Preliminary Vision for a Trail Network

Wildlife Conservation Society

Gainesville, Florida, USA

By Drew Stoll

Contact
Drew Stoll, stolld@edaw.com

Software
ArcInfo, ArcPress, ArcView 3.2, ArcView 3D Analyst, Adobe Photoshop, and Adobe Acrobat

Hardware
Pentium II

Printer
HP DesignJet 1055

Data Source(s)
ESRI Digital Map of the World, Wildlife Conservation Society Mesoamerican Biological Corridor Study, University of Florida GeoPlan Center, U.S. Navy, National Imagery and Mapping Agency, and workshop participants in each country

The Mesoamerican Trails Project aims to establish a system of interconnected trails in Mesoamerica, which would strongly reinforce the principles of nature conservation and cultural heritage preservation in the region. The seven countries of Central America have already embarked upon the establishment of the Mesoamerican Biological Corridor (MBC). Hundreds of individuals were involved in national workshops held in each of the countries. They developed a visionary plan to link together the parks, reserves, and archaeological/historical sites of the MBC with urban areas using a network of hiking, biking, and freshwater and coastal aquatic trails.

Conceptual planning for the trail system involved diagramming the relationship between different landscape features. Relatively small landscape features were represented as dots and/or symbols. Lines were drawn to show the relationship between different locations. As these lines connected more landscape features together, they formed a network of interconnected potential routes or trails. These routes were categorized as arterial, multinational, national, regional, or spur (local) trails. After this conceptual planning was completed, specific routes were chosen for each connector trail.

Visit the Mesoamerican Trails Project Web site at www.wcs.org.

Wildlife Conservation Society

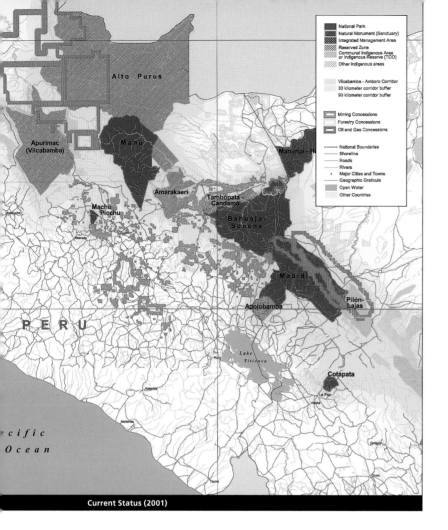

Current Status (2001)

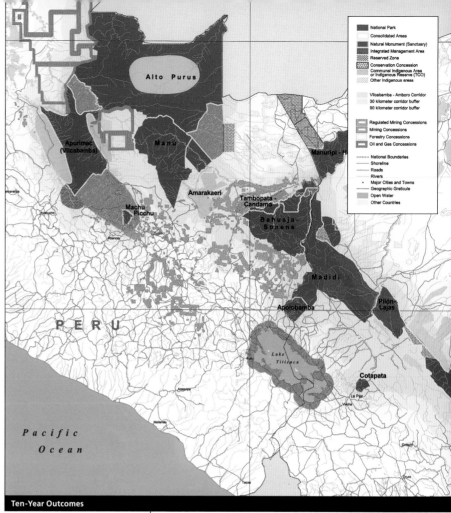

Ten-Year Outcomes

The Vilcabamba–Amboro Conservation Megacorridor is a project of the Andes program of Conservation International (CI). Its goal is to produce a strong, connected, and consolidated zone of biodiversity protection in the eastern slope region of the Andes in South America.

Currently, the area is a patchwork of unconsolidated parks and reserves with significant intrusions of resource extraction concession threats. Plans to mitigate these threats include elimination of major petroleum concessions within the areas of existing parks, implementation of limitations and restrictions on the numerous placer-type gold mining operations, and elimination or conversion to conservation concessions of significant timber extraction zones. Another initiative involves consolidating existing parks (homogenization of protection), upgrading the areas of lesser protection status, and instituting new areas and new types of areas for biodiversity protection.

Conservation International has identified 25 hot spots worldwide for prioritizing biodiversity conservation. In support of these efforts to efficiently preserve global biodiversity, CI's Center for Applied Biodiversity Science (CABS) has invested heavily in the collection, analysis, and publication of data concerning endangered species in these hot spots. Substantial data has been collected in geographic and other database formats, and as the volume of data grows and worldwide demands for information about the hot spots increase, CI and CABS have turned to GIS and digital mapping technologies. The GIS and Mapping Laboratory is the conduit CI and CABS use to marshal and disseminate this data in both electronic and hard-copy form. The GIS and Mapping Laboratory does this by providing conservation mapping and database support services to CI's departments and staff and by developing special GIS projects for the Center for Applied Biodiversity Science.

Vilcabamba–Amboro Conservation Megacorridor—Current Status
Conservation International (CI)
Center for Applied Biodiversity Science
Washington, D.C., USA
By Mark Denil

Contact
Mark Denil, m.denil@conservation.org

Software
ArcView and Windows NT

Printer
HP DesignJet 5000PS

Data Source(s)
Information System of Amazonian Protected Areas, United Nations Food and Agriculture Organization, CI, Global Land Cover Facility, and Digital Chart of the World

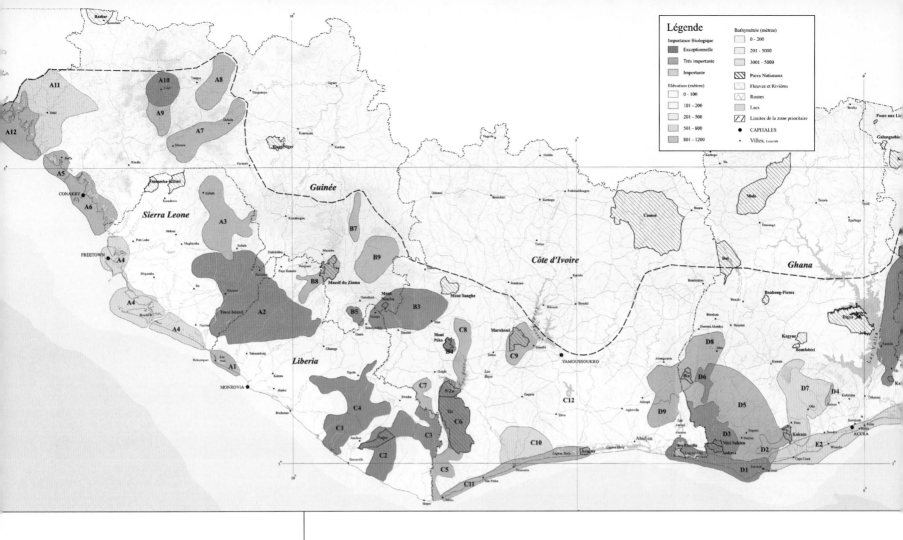

From the Forest to the Sea—Biodiversity Connections from Guinea to Togo

Conservation International

Washington, D.C., USA

By Dirck Byler, Pascale De Souza, Vineet Katariya, Alan Mok, Karen Semkow, Stephen Nash, and Carly Vynne

Contact
Silvio Oliveri, silvio@conservation.org

Software
ArcInfo 7.2.1, ArcView 3.1, Adobe Illustrator 8, Adobe Photoshop 5, and Windows NT

Hardware
Dell workstation

Printer
Offset printer

Data Source(s)
General Bathymetric Chart of the Oceans, British Oceanographic Data Centre, Earth Resources Observation Satellite Data Center, Digital Chart of the World, World Conservation Monitoring Centre, Cartographie & Télédetection, Centre for Resource and Environmental Studies, Australian National University, United Nations Environment Program, Global Resource Information Database, Departament d'Electrònica Informàtica i Automàtica, and World Resources Institute

The Upper Guinea forest is a biologically unique ecosystem and considered one of the world's priority conservation areas because of its high endemism of flora and fauna. One of 25 global hot spots for biodiversity, West Africa's Guinean forest ecosystem has the world's highest diversity of mammals. Forest fragmentation, the result of a variety of socioeconomic factors, threatens the viability of biodiversity in the region. While significant vestiges of the ecosystem's rich biodiversity remain, a once magnificent blanket of forest habitat is threatened. The overall forest ecosystem is approximately 420,000 square kilometers, but estimates of existing forest suggest a loss of nearly 80 percent of the original extent. The remaining forest is highly fragmented and spread across national borders.

This map depicts the scientific consensus on regional priorities for the conservation of biodiversity achieved by 146 experts from 26 countries. The process entailed a one-year compilation of information that culminated in a five-day workshop, verified the state of biodiversity knowledge, and established consensus on the regional conservation priorities across West Africa's globally important humid forest ecosystem and adjacent aquatic ecosystems. The Upper Guinea forest ecosystem along with the adjacent coastal and marine ecosystems was chosen to be the focal point for this exercise. The hot spot boundary (dashed line on the map) provided workshop participants with a geographic limit to define conservation priorities.

The workshop methodology was developed by the facilitator, Conservation International, and has been used in similar workshops in 11 other globally critical ecosystems to enhance conservation planning efforts. This inclusive process aims to enhance conservation efforts in the region by establishing linkages among international and local researchers, institutions, and donors, thereby developing capacity to conserve these critical ecosystems.

This map displays Acadia National Park boundaries, Bar Harbor, Mount Desert, Southwest Harbor and Tremont land use regulatory zones, and private property boundaries. In ArcView, users can click on and identify any land area on Mount Desert Island (MDI). When a user clicks on an area with these layers active, ownership and land protection ordinance data is returned. All land areas on MDI have protective measures in place whether they are privately owned, municipal, or national park lands.

Data layers shown on this map were developed by College of the Atlantic students for the listed entities. Students worked with local officials in selecting and designing color schemes for the official town maps, and official town map colors are represented on this map. This map has been well accepted by the island community and is the only map that shows the island as a whole. One purpose of this map was to promote an understanding of cross-boundary land protection issues and a more holistic way of looking at the island.

College of the Atlantic would like to pay tribute to one of the map authors, Kurt Jacobsen, who recently passed away, and the late Ian McHarg, landscape architect, mentor, spiritual advisor, and giant in the environmental movement.

Mount Desert Island Land Protection and Ownership

College of the Atlantic, GIS Laboratory

Bar Harbor, Maine, USA

By Lalania Avila, Michael Blair, Jana Butts, Kurt Jacobsen, Gordon Longsworth, Glen Mittlehauser, and Rick Schauffler, College of the Atlantic; Karen Anderson and Mike Blaney, Acadia National Park; and John Brushwein, John Lockman, Jean Marshall, Gretchen Strong, and Patty Tierny, Town of Bar Harbor

Contact
Gordon Longsworth, gordonL@ecology.coa.edu

Software
ArcView 3.2a and Windows NT 4.0

Printer
HP DesignJet 650C

Data Source(s)
U.S. Geological Survey, Maine Office of GIS, municipal tax parcel and zoning maps, and Acadia National Park land status maps

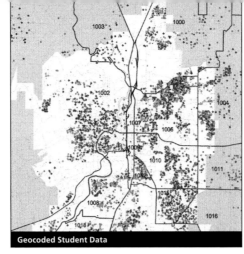

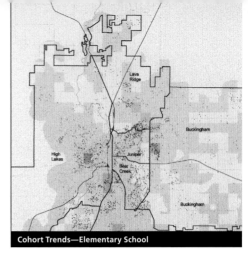

Geocoded Student Data

Cohort Trends—Elementary School

	01/KG	02/01	03/02	04/03	05/04	06/05	07/07	08/09	10/09	10/09	11/10	12/11
89-90	1.53	1.01	1.07	1.09	1.06	1.13	1.03	1.09	1.12	0.96	0.97	0.92
90-91	1.33	1.01	1.01	1.08	1.04	1.09	1.04	1.03	1.02	0.97	0.94	0.92
91-92	1.25	0.99	1.04	1.03	1.02	1.09	1.04	1.03	1.06	1.03	0.96	0.93
92-93	1.25	1.00	1.06	1.05	1.04	1.06	1.00	1.02	1.02	1.01	0.95	0.92
93-94	1.20	1.06	1.05	1.06	1.02	1.09	1.08	1.01	1.04	1.00	0.93	0.92
94-95	1.14	1.05	1.02	1.04	1.02	0.99	1.03	1.00	1.08	1.00	0.98	0.87
95-96	1.16	1.03	1.03	1.02	1.04	1.05	1.07	1.06	1.10	1.01	0.96	0.94
96-97	1.13	1.03	1.03	1.05	1.06	1.02	1.04	1.03	1.05	0.97	0.93	0.93
97-98	1.13	1.05	1.06	1.04	1.03	1.01	1.04	1.00	1.08	1.01	0.94	0.88
98-99	1.15	1.04	1.02	1.01	1.03	1.04	1.06	1.04	1.12	0.99	0.98	0.95

Cohort Trends—Bend–LaPine School District

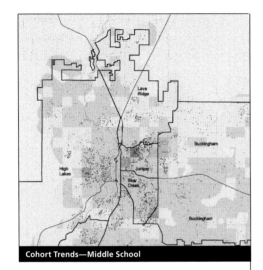

Cohort Trends—Middle School

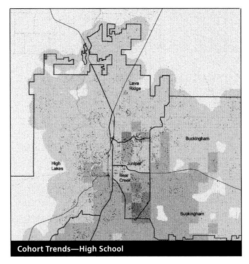

Cohort Trends—High School

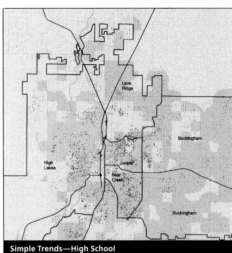

Simple Trends—High School

**GIS in School Enrollment Forecasting—
An Example for Bend, Oregon**
Portland State University

Portland, Oregon, USA

By Richard Lycan

Contact
Deane Lycan, lycand@pdx.edu

Software
ArcView 3.2, Microsoft Excel, and Windows NT 4.0

Printer
HP DesignJet 750CM/PS

Data Source(s)
School enrollment data and county GIS data

Deschutes County and the Bend–LaPine School District are two of the most rapidly growing areas in Oregon. One result of this growth has been the need for more schools. The school district sought a $45.7 million bond to acquire six new school sites and build three new schools. The district contracted with David Evans and Associates (DEA) for planning support. DEA approached the Population Research Center (PRC) at Portland State University for assistance in forecasting future school enrollment. This poster shows part of that work by PRC, particularly some of the facets that depended heavily on the use of GIS tools.

This map illustrates the use of one type of model used for school enrollment forecasting, the grade progression model. The graphs show how this model is conventionally applied to a districtwide population. The maps show how this model can be applied to small geographical areas with spatial trending using ArcView Spatial Analyst and other tools.

The graph shows the conventional application of the grade progression model to the entire school district. The value of 1.53 in the upper left cell of the graph indicates that there were 1.53 times as many first grade students in 1990 as there were kindergarten students in 1989. Areas shown in shades of red on this graph indicate increases in a grade cohort from one year to the next. Areas in blue indicate declines. Similarly, the maps of cohort trends display trends from 1997 to 1999, showing areas of gains in red and areas of losses in blue. ArcView Spatial Analyst was used to transform the geocoded point student data to a grid map of generalized trends.

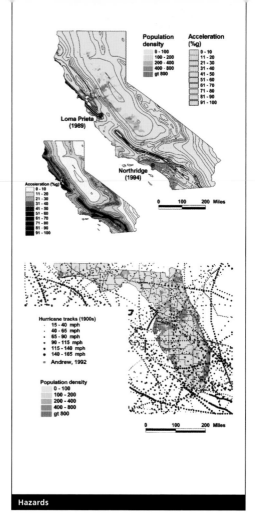

Hazards

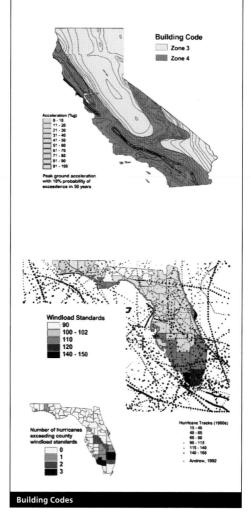

Building Codes

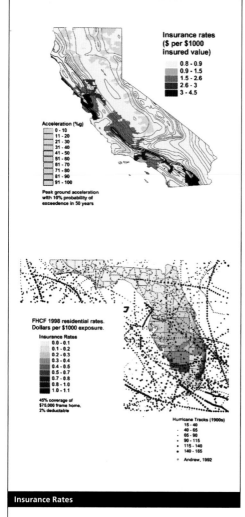

Insurance Rates

The costs of natural disasters in the United States are increasing despite a better understanding of the process and advances in the technologies available to mitigate them. During the period of 1989 to 1998, the majority of the Federal Emergency Management Agency's disaster relief dollars went to two states. California received 43 percent, and Florida received 10 percent. Using these two states as case studies, the authors chose 1998 as a snapshot in time to look at California's response to the 1994 Northridge earthquake and Florida's reaction to Hurricane Andrew in 1992.

With a range of hazards, California has just two levels of building codes. In Florida, the hazard is more constant, but there is a wide range of building codes. The building codes do not correlate with our knowledge of risk. California has a wide range of risk but a small range in insurance rates. Florida is the reverse with a small range in risk but large range in rates. For both insurance rates and building codes, Florida's and California's response appears to be the reverse of what they should be. It appears that both states are responding to the last event rather than mitigating against the next event. Florida is hit by a hurricane every year resulting in high-resolution variations in mitigation. California's earthquakes occur less frequently hence a smaller range in building codes and insurance rates.

The relationship of mitigation to distance from the most recent events is particularly clear for Florida where both the insurance rates and building code standards diminish with distance from the Hurricane Andrew track (shown as red dots). The reason for this is that most mitigation strategies require legislation. Legislation requires public support. Public support requires awareness of the risk. Public awareness requires an event—a disaster. Fully exploiting our current understanding of risk to develop mitigation strategies will serve to prepare the public for future disasters.

This work is part of research done by Princeton undergraduate students.

Does the United States Need More Natural Disasters?

Princeton University Geosciences Department

Princeton, New Jersey, USA

By Geff Adamson, Richard M. Allen, Cathy Bell, Justin Bennett, Brooke Doherty, Kate Fleeger, Jon Gordon, Heather Hibbert, Neal Jagtab, Bill Langin, W. Jason Morgan, Mike Pishioneri, Kevin Roberts, T. Wangyal Shawa, and Gregory E. van der Vink

Contact
T. Wangyal Shawa, shawatw@princeton.edu

Software
ArcView, Adobe Illustrator, and Windows NT

Hardware
Dell workstation

Printer
HP DesignJet 1055CM

Data Source(s)
U.S. Census Bureau and others

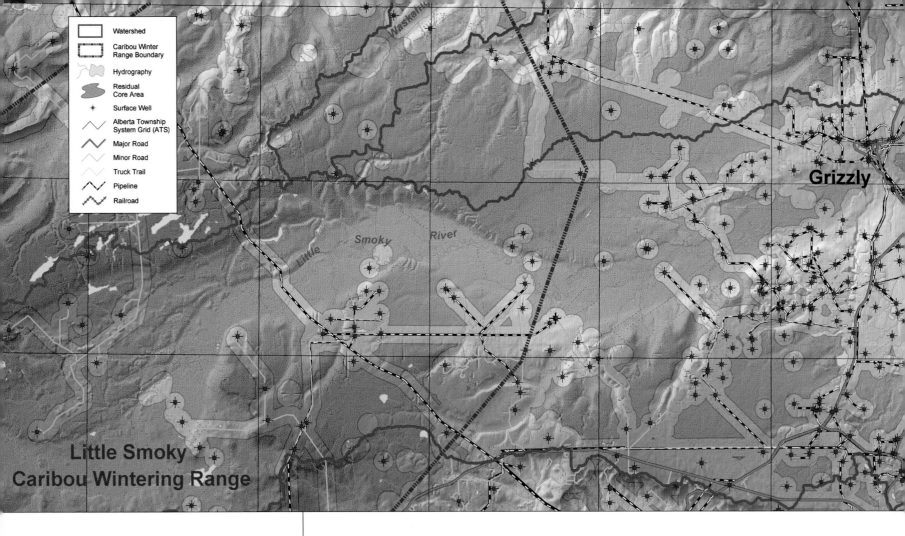

Little Smoky Caribou Wintering Range

Grizzly

Legend:
- Watershed
- Caribou Winter Range Boundary
- Hydrography
- Residual Core Area
- Surface Well
- Alberta Township System Grid (ATS)
- Major Road
- Minor Road
- Truck Trail
- Pipeline
- Railroad

Cumulative Effects Assessment (CEA)— Disturbance Mapping

GAIA Consultants Inc.

Calgary, Alberta, Canada

By Jake Gagnon and Mel Vanderwal

Contact
Jake Gagnon, jake.gagnon@gaiaenv.com

Software:
ArcInfo 8.1, ArcView 3.2, CEAnalyst, and PCI OrthoEngine 8.2

Hardware
AMD Athlon XP 1800+

Printer
HP DesignJet 750C+

Data Source(s)
AltaLIS, Ltd.; Boyd Geomatics; Salmo Consulting Inc.; and GAIA Consultants Inc.

Consideration of cumulative environmental effects is an evolving practice. GAIA Consultants Inc., in conjunction with Salmo Consulting Inc., has worked closely with a multitude of stakeholders to identify the current landscape status and potential project impacts in a region of western Alberta, Canada. Results from this analysis were used to understand better cumulative effects in the region and to address regulatory inquiries.

This map displays some of the results of a landscape-based modeling exercise for a major Canadian energy company. Landscape indexes for existing and future conditions were calculated using a customized application, CEAnalyst, built by GAIA using ArcView 3.2 and ArcInfo 8.1 software and linked via remote procedure call. ArcInfo acted as a server engine responding to spatial manipulation requests sent by the ArcView client.

Anthropogenic features were identified and classified using recent orthorectified aerial photography. Features were widened based on class median feature widths derived from the orthorectified photography and were integrated into the existing landscape using the CEAnalyst extension. A suite of index values were calculated in ArcView based on ecologically meaningful metrics that were compared to thresholds, assessment criteria, and management plans. The CEAnalyst extension then used Dynamic Data Exchange to pass tabular results into a formatted spreadsheet in which subsequent analyses were undertaken.

Residual core areas are shown here, transparently overlaid on a hillshade and elevation model using ArcMap 8.1.

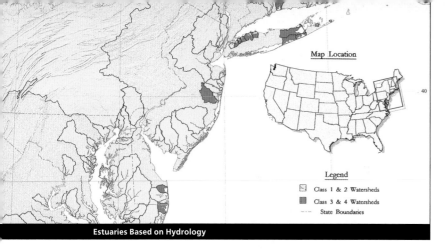

Estuaries Based on Hydrology

Map Location

Legend

Class 1 & 2 Watersheds
Class 3 & 4 Watersheds
State Boundaries

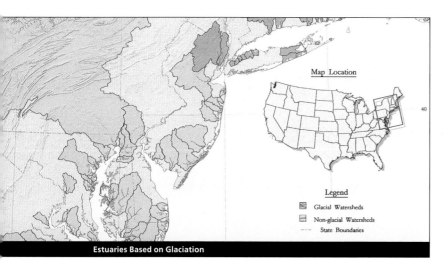

Estuaries Based on Glaciation

Map Location

Legend

Glacial Watersheds
Non-glacial Watersheds
State Boundaries

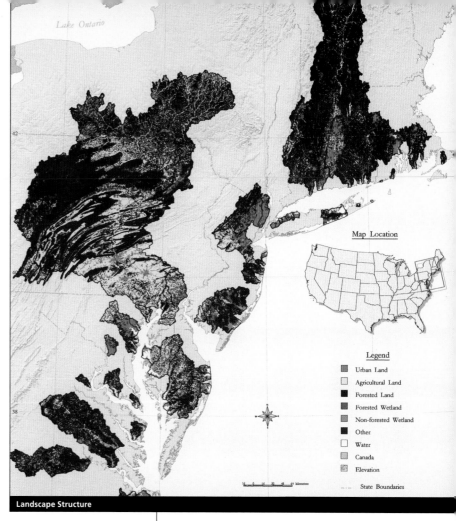

Landscape Structure

Map Location

Legend

Urban Land
Agricultural Land
Forested Land
Forested Wetland
Non-forested Wetland
Other
Water
Canada
Elevation
State Boundaries

Congressional amendments to the Clean Water Act have shifted emphasis on control of pollution in the United States from point to nonpoint sources. Runoff from land is a major source of nonpoint pollution. Recent studies helped to develop landscape metrics for measuring landscape characteristics. The quantitative relationships between landscape metrics and sediment contamination in small estuaries in the Mid-Atlantic and southern New England regions of the United States were developed to determine which metrics are appropriate for predicting the impact of nonpoint pollution on estuarine waters.

The measurements of nine metals collected at the Virginian Province sampling locations were selected for consideration as dependent variables. Principal components analysis was used to assess the relationship among individual sediment contaminants and to reduce the number of variables for statistical modeling. Land cover pattern was used as a surrogate for nonpoint source pollution. For this study, land cover type refers to the composition of land cover types within a watershed. ArcInfo was used to determine the area of each land cover class found within each watershed. Six landscape metrics for each watershed were calculated: area, percent urban land, percent forested land, percent forested wetlands, percent nonforested wetlands, and percent agricultural land.

The results indicate that inclusion of terms to account for watershed/estuarine processes to mitigate the effect of the watershed stressors is important. The glacial or hydrological variables were more important to include as categorical variables than as additional additive independent variables. All models indicated that sediment contamination was strongly influenced by percent urban land (positive) and percent forested or nonforested wetlands (negative). The overall results from this study are indicative of how statistical models can be developed by relating landscape metrics to estuarine contamination.

Landscape Structure and Estuarine Condition in the Mid-Atlantic and Southern New England Region of the United States

U.S. Environmental Protection Agency

Narragansett, Rhode Island, USA

By Randy Comeleo, third author; Jane Copeland, first author; and John Paul, second author

Contact
Jane Copeland, copeland.jane@epa.gov

Software
ArcInfo 8.1 and Windows NT

Printer
HP DesignJet 3500CP

Data Source(s)
National land cover data

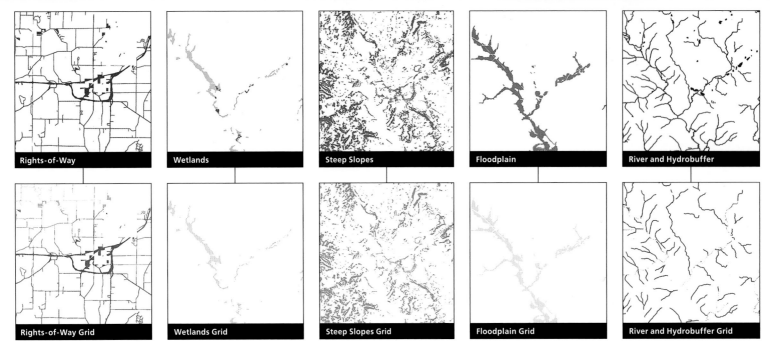

| Rights-of-Way | Wetlands | Steep Slopes | Floodplain | River and Hydrobuffer |

| Rights-of-Way Grid | Wetlands Grid | Steep Slopes Grid | Floodplain Grid | River and Hydrobuffer Grid |

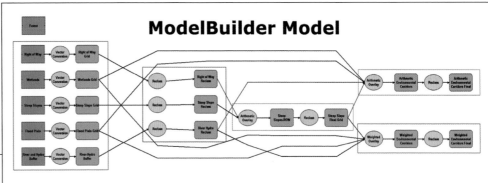

ModelBuilder Model

Defining Environmental Corridors in Verona Township, Wisconsin, Using ModelBuilder

University of Wisconsin–Madison, Land Information and Computer Graphics Facility

Madison, Wisconsin, USA

By Jennifer Hansen

Contact
Jennifer Hansen, jlhanse3@facstaff.wisc.edu

Software
ArcView 3.2, ArcView Spatial Analyst, ModelBuilder™, and Windows NT 4.0

Printer
HP DesignJet 2500

Data Source(s)
Wisconsin Department of Natural Resources, Dane County Land Information Office, and Federal Emergency Management Agency

This model is used to define environmental corridors in a study area in Dane County, Wisconsin. The study area encompasses Verona Township and a one-mile buffer of the township. The model begins with five shapefiles that are converted to grids. Four of the shapefiles are the basic features of environmental corridors—steep slopes, wetlands, rivers, and hydro buffer.

Two other features are included. Rights-of-way is added to remove steep slopes that are created as the result of road embankments, and floodplain is added to consider the dynamic pathways that are created over time within a water system.

Rights-of-way, steep slopes, river, and hydro buffer are reclassified to define where the features exist within the study area. When the locations of the features are established, steep slopes that fall within rights-of-way are removed from the analysis, and the grid is reclassified to reflect the changes.

Two environmental corridors grids create the final results. The arithmetic environmental corridors final contains areas that have any occurrence of the environmental corridors features. The weighted environmental corridors final applies weights within and among the features so that priorities can be assigned to higher ranked corridors.

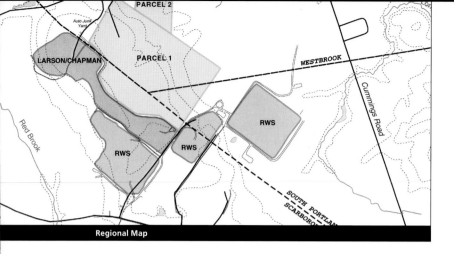

Regional Map

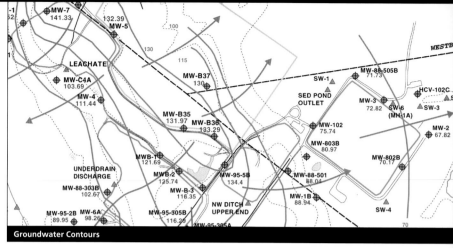

Groundwater Contours

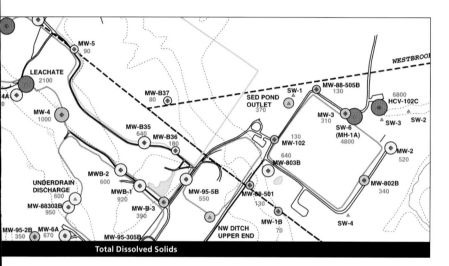

Total Dissolved Solids

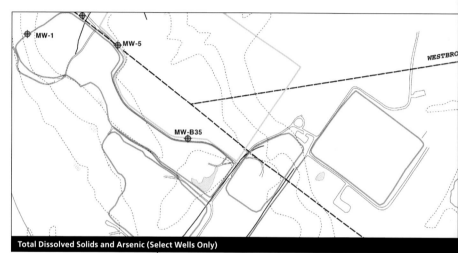

Total Dissolved Solids and Arsenic (Select Wells Only)

This series of maps displays information on the groundwater conditions in and around the proposed Pine Tree Waste transfer station near Portland, Maine. The application to develop the transfer station was opposed by a competitor within the same industry, and the Maine Board of Environmental Protection was charged with reviewing the permit application and the opposition against it. To prepare a summary of groundwater conditions near the transfer station, Maine Department of Environmental Protection (MEDEP) staff georeferenced spatial data in the MEDEP GIS system. Statewide data layers developed by the Maine Office of GIS were used in the background, and MEDEP staff gathered data on water level elevations and chemical concentrations in monitoring wells used in other water quality monitoring programs.

The Regional map shows the regional relationships of the area's topographic and drainage features to the solid waste facilities and the proposed transfer facility. Because it is located within a drainage divide, it was determined that the landfill would not have an effect on the study area groundwater conditions. The Groundwater Contours map shows the groundwater contours under the study area.

The Total Dissolved Solids (TDS) map shows the distribution of total dissolved solids in monitoring wells at the Larson–Chapman and Regional Waste Systems, Inc. (RWS), facilities. TDS provides a general indication of the presence and magnitude of contamination due to inorganic chemical parameters such as metals. The map of Total Dissolved Solids and Arsenic depicts four of the Larson–Chapman monitoring wells with associated time series plots of TDS and arsenic. These plots are used to show trends, either upward or downward, in concentrations of the two indicator parameters.

Along with MEDEP staff testimony, the maps helped impart a large amount of complicated information in a short period. The board was able to make a highly informed decision based on the best information available.

Maine Groundwater Map Series
Maine Department of Environmental Protection

Augusta, Maine, USA

By John P. Lynam

Contact
John Lynam, john.lynam@state.me.us

Software
ArcInfo 8 and Microsoft Excel

Hardware
Dell PowerEdge 6300, Sun Enterprise 4500, and StorEdge A5200

Printer
Xerox Phaser 790

Data Source(s)
Maine Department of Environmental Protection, Maine Office of GIS, Sevee and Maher Engineers, Woodard and Curran, and St. Germain and Associates

Maine Department of Environmental Protection

Cedar River Municipal Watershed
Road Deconstruction

City of Seattle, Seattle Public Utilities, Watershed Management Division

North Bend, Washington, USA

By Tom Van Buren

Contact
Tom Van Buren, vanburt@ci.seattle.wa.us

Software
ArcInfo 8.0.1

Hardware
Sun Ultra 80

Printer
HP DesignJet 2500

Data Source(s)
Washington Department of Natural Resources, King County GIS, U.S. Geological Survey, and City of Seattle

These maps are part of a cartography series published by the Watershed Management Division and are generated via Inter-Application Communication using Perl scripts and HTML forms to execute several ARC Macro Language programs. Cartography such as this and dynamic access to it help support daily operations and long-term programs of the division.

The Cedar River Watershed Habitat Conservation Plan (HCP) is a 50-year, ecosystem-based plan that will cost Seattle ratepayers approximately $90 million to implement. It ensures Seattle's drinking water supply and protects and restores the habitats of 83 species of fish and wildlife that could be affected by water supply and hydroelectric operations on the Cedar River. The plan includes land and forest management in the municipal watershed, mitigation for the blockage to anadromous salmon and trout at the city's drinking water intake, regulation of stream flows in the Cedar River, and research and monitoring to support conservation and mitigation measures.

Road deconstruction is a large component of the HCP. Forest road engineers use dynamic segmentation (and an interactive event editor) to update and plan road operations. Two hundred miles of road is targeted for removal or deconstruction by 2020.

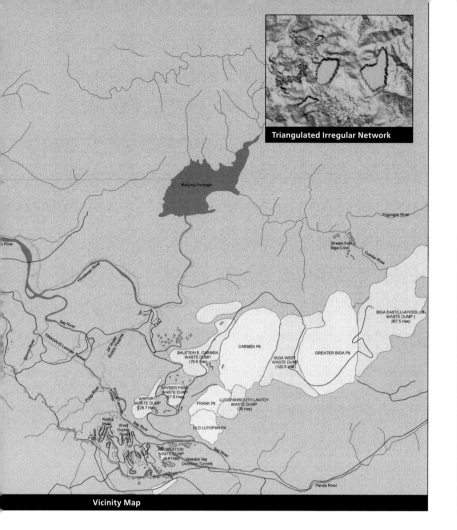

Triangulated Irregular Network

Vicinity Map

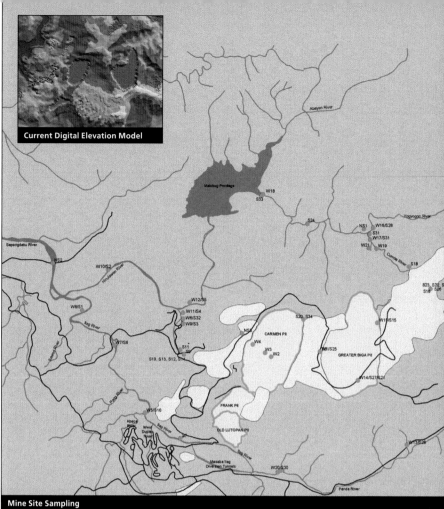

Current Digital Elevation Model

Mine Site Sampling

Atlas Mine, located on the Philippine island of Cebu, was a producing copper mine from 1953 to 1994. When mining activity ceased, the remaining ore, waste dumps, and infrastructure began to decay and cause significant environmental damage. Following a major fish kill in 1999, a study was funded to assess damage and provide remediation guidelines.

The main contributor to pollution is acid rock drainage (ARD), which happens when the sulfide minerals in rocks and mine waste dissolve in water. Atlas has four abandoned open pits. Water from the region's intense rainfall collects in them and flows into a number of river systems and ultimately into Tanon Strait. Image processing was used to identify potential areas of ARD and to determine sites for fieldwork and sampling of soil and water. Landsat derivatives delineated contaminated areas and surface geology. On-site sampling of water, soil, and biology took place in the dry season and again in the wet season, and the results were analyzed in GIS. Toxicology of biology samples was also mapped in a more general manner, averaged along stretches of river and ocean.

Remediation measures must be cost-effective while maximizing beneficial socioeconomic outcomes for the region. Spatial analysis of slopes will enable native plantings or wall construction to stabilize slopes and minimize runoff. ARD can be reduced by the simple addition of limestone or lime to affected water bodies. Investigation of geology maps and Landsat images shows abundant limestone deposits in the region, and it is possible that the production of limestone and activated clay mineral products will provide employment for local workers during long-term remediation.

A digital atlas combining topographic, sampling, and infrastructure data has been created, which provides a basis for ongoing fieldwork and basic asset management—assets that are contributing to pollution and those that could be used to benefit local citizens such as the medical center.

Assessing and Remediation of the Environmental Damage at a Former Copper Mine Site
Maunsell Australia Pty. Ltd.

Milton, Queensland, Australia

By Robyn Gallagher

Contact
Robyn Gallagher, robyn.gallagher@maunsell.com.au

Software
ArcView 3 and Windows NT

Printer
HP DesignJet 750

Data Source(s)
Hard-copy mine maps, field surveys, and Landsat images

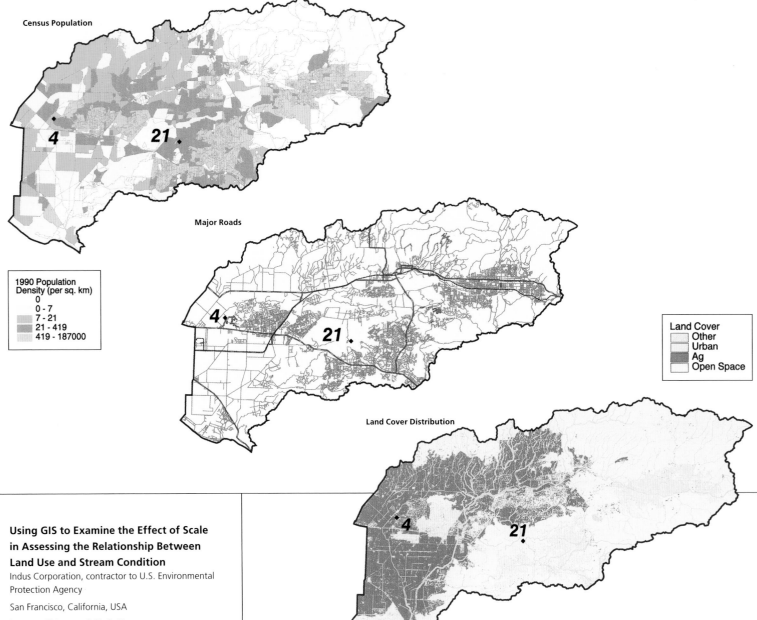

Census Population

Major Roads

Land Cover Distribution

1990 Population
Density (per sq. km)
0
0 - 7
7 - 21
21 - 419
419 - 187000

Land Cover
Other
Urban
Ag
Open Space

Using GIS to Examine the Effect of Scale in Assessing the Relationship Between Land Use and Stream Condition

Indus Corporation, contractor to U.S. Environmental Protection Agency

San Francisco, California, USA

By Dean Chiang and Cindy Lin

Contact
Cheryl Henley, henley.cheryl@epa.gov

Software
ArcView 3.2 and Solaris 2.7

Hardware
Sun Ultra 1 workstation

Printer
HP DesignJet 1055

Data Source(s)
National Elevation Dataset, National Hydrography Dataset, National Land Cover Dataset, and U.S. Census Bureau

Landscape modifications due to agricultural needs, urban sprawl, and intensive population growth have seriously reshaped the stream hydrology and ecology in Southern California. This study examines the effects of dominant land uses on stream condition in the Calleguas Creek Watershed. To understand the effects of land use on the stream ecology, analysts evaluated how the observed field condition (e.g., fish, benthic macro invertebrates, and riparian habitat) corresponds to landscape indicators such as land cover percentages (urban, agriculture, and open space), population density, and road density.

They first defined the associated land use to each stream site by describing the type of land use encountered immediately adjacent to the sites. It is clear that exclusively describing the adjacent land uses to a stream site will not encompass all land use activities affecting the sampling site (e.g., agricultural field irrigation discharging into the stream way flows through all downstream tributaries). This study explores how scale and different land use definitions may affect landscape indicator estimation.

EJ Score
- Unpopulated
- Zero
- One
- Two
- Three
- Four
- Five
- Six
- Seven

EPA Regulated Site
- △ Site not in Area of EJ Concern
- ▲ Site in Area of EJ Concern

In fiscal year 1992, the U.S. Environmental Protection Agency (EPA)–New England designated environmental justice (EJ) as a key priority area for strategic planning purposes. EJ embraces the belief that no segment of the population should bear a disproportionate share of the consequences of environmental pollution. EJ is defined by EPA as the fair treatment and meaningful involvement of all people regardless of race, color, national origin, or income with respect to the development, implementation, and enforcement of environmental laws, regulations, and policies.

In 1993, EPA–New England created a methodology (currently under review) for mapping demographic characteristics of the region using GIS to identify potential EJ areas. Two scores are assigned to each census block group in the region—one based on the percentage of its population that is minority and the other based on the percentage of its population that is low-income. These two scores are added together to create a ranking of potential EJ area.

This map is an example of how environmental data can be overlaid with the potential EJ scores of an area to characterize the environmental burden in a given community. Point features on the map are facilities regulated under the EPA's Resource Conservation and Recovery Act and the Comprehensive Environmental Response, Compensation, and Liability Act (Superfund) programs. This information is typically used to aid in the prioritization of EPA inspections, actions, and follow-ups.

Assessing Environmental Justice

U.S. Environmental Protection Agency (EPA)–New England/SIGNAL Corporation

Boston, Massachusetts, USA

By Christine Foot

Contact
Christine Foot, foot.christine@epa.gov

Software
ArcGIS 8.1 and Windows NT 4.0

Hardware
Dell OptiPlex GX110

Printer
HP DesignJet 750C

Data Source(s)
U.S. Census Bureau and U.S. EPA

SAN DIEGO COUNTY

NO ELEVATION DATA

691 Transmission Line

Utility Infrastructure—Camp Pendleton

Sempra Energy Utilities

San Diego, California, USA

By Casey Cook

Contact
Casey Cook, ccook@sempra.com

Software
ArcMap 8.1 and ArcGIS Spatial Analyst

Hardware
Compaq AP 550

Printer
HP DesignJet 2500CP

Data Source(s)
San Diego Gas and Electric, Camp Pendleton, and San Diego Geographic Information Source

This digital elevation model (DEM) was created from one- to two-foot contours that were merged from 50 map sheets. The contours were converted into a DEM with five-foot cell resolution. A hillshade was derived from the DEM and used as a backdrop with environmental, transportation, utility, and computer-aided design (CAD) data layers. CAD data was imported directly into ArcMap and symbolized. Environmental and transportation data sets were ArcInfo coverages. The labeling tools in ArcMap enabled extensive labeling of the utility infrastructure and how it relates to the sensitive species information.

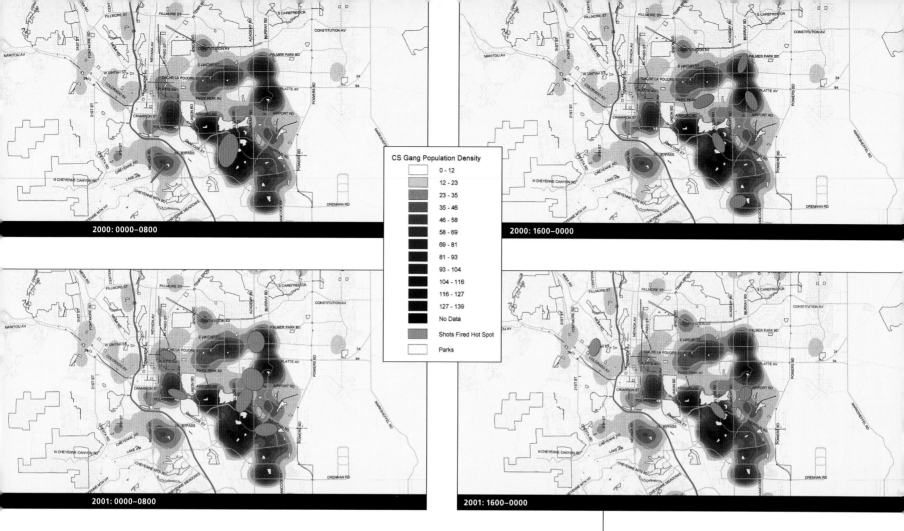

CS Gang Population Density

- 0 – 12
- 12 – 23
- 23 – 35
- 35 – 46
- 46 – 58
- 58 – 69
- 69 – 81
- 81 – 93
- 93 – 104
- 104 – 116
- 116 – 127
- 127 – 139
- No Data
- Shots Fired Hot Spot
- Parks

2000: 0000–0800

2000: 1600–0000

2001: 0000–0800

2001: 1600–0000

In 2001, the Colorado Springs Police Department had experienced a larger than normal volume of "shots fired" calls for service. This type of call involves citizens' and officers' reports of unidentified gunfire, in which gunshots or what is perceived to be gunshots are heard with little or no other information available. The analysis was done in April to evaluate resources for the coming summer months, which are typically busier.

The first part of the analysis involved creating hot spots by time of day using ArcView 3.1 for three segments of a 24-hour day (from 0000 to 0800, 0800 to 1600, and 1600 to 0000) and then looking for a consistent correlation among hot spots based on time of day and between the year and geographic location. The views were created for these time slots for the first quarter of the years 2000 and 2001. For hot spots, the shots fired calls for service were extracted from the calls for service database and applied to the map. Address locations were used as a point theme. The CrimeStat application formed the hot spots based on the ArcView shapefile. The criteria used for each hot spot was 10 or more shots fired calls approximately 100 feet from one another during the referenced time frame. The result showed several geographic relationships in the 1600 to 0000 period and the 0000 to 0800 period.

Next, regions in Colorado Springs were analyzed to determine if there were other contributing factors to the problem with shots fired calls. Several density grids were generated based on varying factors including housing, schools, parks, and the gang residential population. The analysis revealed that there was a significant relationship between the shots fired calls for service and the street gang residential addresses in Colorado Springs. The hot spots aligned with the more dense sections of the street gang member residential addresses. This information was useful to the department in planning resources for the upcoming summer months and gave staff another look at street gang activity in Colorado Springs.

Colorado Springs Police Department—Shots Fired

Colorado Springs Police Department

Colorado Springs, Colorado, USA

By Karen Lincoln

Contact

Karen Lincoln, lincolka@ci.colospgs.co.us

Software

ArcView 3.1, CrimeStat 1.0, and Windows NT

Printer

HP DesignJet 1050C

Data Source(s)

Colorado Springs Police Department Calls for Service and Criminal Justice Information System

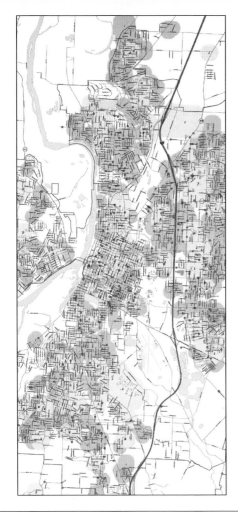

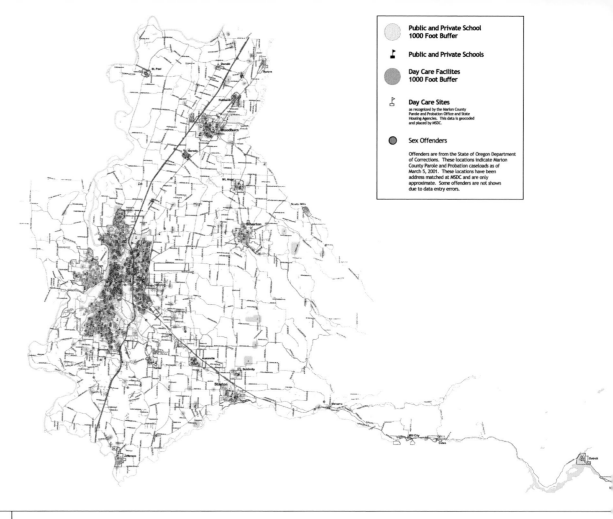

Public and Private School
1000 Foot Buffer

Public and Private Schools

Day Care Facilites
1000 Foot Buffer

Day Care Sites
as recognized by the Marion County
Parole and Probation Office and State
Housing Agencies. This data is geocoded
and placed by MSDC.

Sex Offenders
Offenders are from the State of Oregon Department
of Corrections. These locations indicate Marion
County Parole and Probation caseloads as of
March 5, 2001. These locations have been
address matched at MSDC and are only
approximate. Some offenders are not shown
due to data entry errors.

Salem/Keizer Sex Offenders—
Schools and Child Care Centers with
1,000-Foot Buffer Zones

Marion/Salem Geographic Information System

Salem, Oregon, USA

By Daniel Brown

Contact
Daniel Brown, dbrown@open.org

Software
ArcView 3.2 and Windows NT 4.0

Printer
HP DesignJet 650

Data Source(s)
Marion/Salem GIS; State of Oregon Department of
Corrections; and Marion County, Oregon

This project was prompted by Oregon House Bill 2503, which is designed to prohibit sex offenders from living within 1,000 feet from schools, day care centers, parks, playgrounds, and/or other places where minors gather.

This map was made to demonstrate the significance of the bill to the county law enforcement and state legislatures. The Marion County Parole and Probation Department requested this analysis to review the impacts of the legislation. With the assistance of state day care databases, the Oregon Department of Corrections offender data, and the Marion/Salem GIS, these maps helped to define House Bill 2503 at the local level. They clearly display a visual rendition of sex offender residences and how they are related to schools and day care centers within Marion County.

City, county, and state leaders were informed about offenders' spatial relationships to schools and child care facilities with accurate and visual information that assists them as they make decisions about future Oregon laws.

Incidents per Address

HOT SPOTS

low crime   high crime

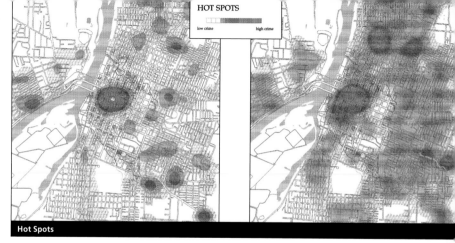

Hot Spots

RATE CHANGE

decrease   increase

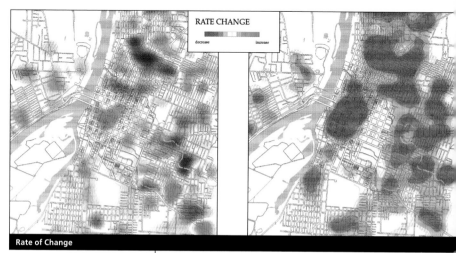

Rate of Change

There is ongoing cooperation between the Salem Police Department and the Marion/Salem Data Center. This effort is focused on the development of spatial incident and dispatch data. With ESRI® tools, such as ArcView at the police department and ArcInfo at the Marion/Salem Data Center, the crime reporting capabilities have evolved to include gang tracking, hot spot analysis, and neighborhood reporting. Within the Salem Police Department, these capabilities are performed in the Planning and Research Unit.

The Planning and Research Unit of the Salem Police Department is dedicated to providing citizens with quality information and service. These maps can help in the assessment of Salem's crime problem areas, assist in identifying crime trends, and keep Salem citizens informed about crime in their community. The selected incidents shown on these maps represent major incidents as defined by the Salem Police Department. These persons and property crimes are considered citizen-concerned types of incidents.

The police department does crime management and planning at the neighborhood level and citywide. On a monthly basis, crime statistics are tracked and reported for 19 different neighborhood associations. These reports are provided to Salem citizens through community meetings and www.cityofsalem.net.

The Salem Police Department and Marion/Salem Data Center are constantly enhancing and updating procedures to provide advanced analytical support for collecting, analyzing, and disseminating timely, accurate, and useful information describing crime patterns, crime trends, and potential suspects. This vision and planning will assist Salem in maintaining its high quality of life and safe communities.

City of Salem, Oregon, Major Crime Incidents Report for April 2001
Marion/Salem Data Center

Salem, Oregon, USA

By Daniel Brown

Contact
Daniel Brown, dbrown@open.org

Software
ArcInfo 7.2, ArcView, and UNIX

Hardware
HP

Printer
HP DesignJet 650

Data Source(s)
Marion/Salem GIS and Regional SUN/RAIN Systems

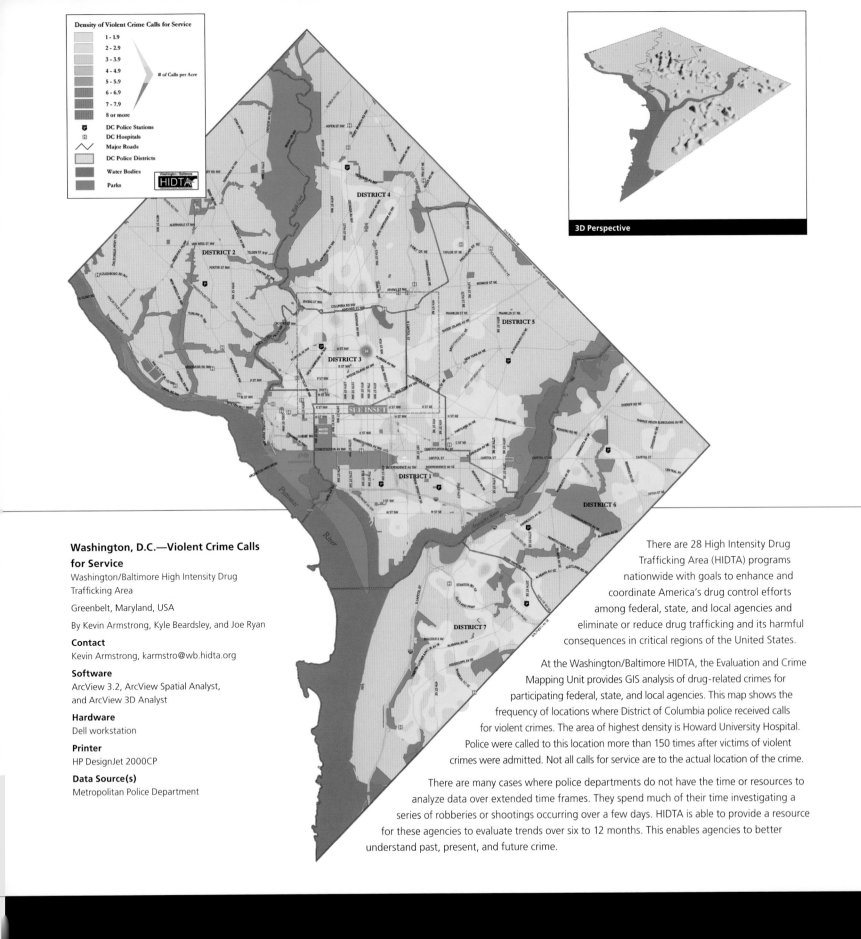

Density of Violent Crime Calls for Service

- 1 - 1.9
- 2 - 2.9
- 3 - 3.9
- 4 - 4.9
- 5 - 5.9
- 6 - 6.9
- 7 - 7.9
- 8 or more

# of Calls per Acre

- DC Police Stations
- DC Hospitals
- Major Roads
- DC Police Districts
- Water Bodies
- Parks

3D Perspective

DISTRICT 4

DISTRICT 2

DISTRICT 5

DISTRICT 3

SEE INSET

WHITE HOUSE

DISTRICT 1

DISTRICT 6

DISTRICT 7

Potomac River

Anacostia River

Washington, D.C.—Violent Crime Calls for Service

Washington/Baltimore High Intensity Drug
Trafficking Area

Greenbelt, Maryland, USA

By Kevin Armstrong, Kyle Beardsley, and Joe Ryan

Contact
Kevin Armstrong, karmstro@wb.hidta.org

Software
ArcView 3.2, ArcView Spatial Analyst,
and ArcView 3D Analyst

Hardware
Dell workstation

Printer
HP DesignJet 2000CP

Data Source(s)
Metropolitan Police Department

There are 28 High Intensity Drug
Trafficking Area (HIDTA) programs
nationwide with goals to enhance and
coordinate America's drug control efforts
among federal, state, and local agencies and
eliminate or reduce drug trafficking and its harmful
consequences in critical regions of the United States.

At the Washington/Baltimore HIDTA, the Evaluation and Crime
Mapping Unit provides GIS analysis of drug-related crimes for
participating federal, state, and local agencies. This map shows the
frequency of locations where District of Columbia police received calls
for violent crimes. The area of highest density is Howard University Hospital.
Police were called to this location more than 150 times after victims of violent
crimes were admitted. Not all calls for service are to the actual location of the crime.

There are many cases where police departments do not have the time or resources to
analyze data over extended time frames. They spend much of their time investigating a
series of robberies or shootings occurring over a few days. HIDTA is able to provide a resource
for these agencies to evaluate trends over six to 12 months. This enables agencies to better
understand past, present, and future crime.

Tornado at Benbrook: Mostly Single-Family homes | Southwest Fort Worth: Homes and Apartments - High Average Values | East Fort Worth: Large Structure Count - Home and Commercial Mix | Downtown Fort Worth: Low Structure Count - Very High Commercial Value | Near TCJC NE Campus: Very Large Number of Apartment Units

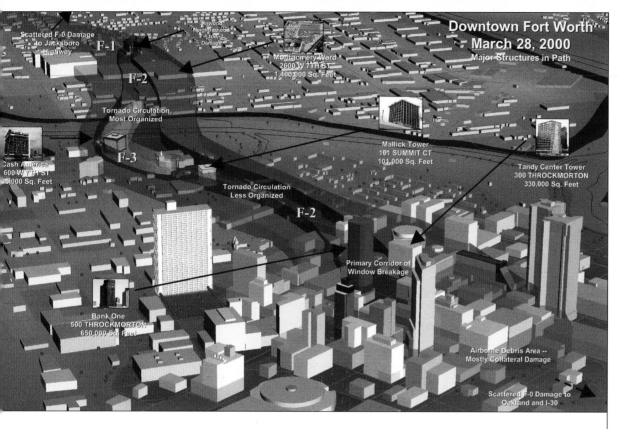

Downtown Fort Worth
March 28, 2000
Major Structures in Path

Scattered F-0 Damage to Jacksboro Highway

F-1

F-2

Linwood Neighborhood Minor Damage

Montgomery Ward 2600 W 7TH ST 1,400,000 Sq. Feet

Tornado Circulation Most Organized

Cash America 600 W 7TH ST 251,000 Sq. Feet

F-3

Mallick Tower 101 SUMMIT CT 101,000 Sq. Feet

Tandy Center Tower 300 THROCKMORTON 330,000 Sq. Feet

Tornado Circulation Less Organized

F-2

Bank One 500 THROCKMORTON 650,000 Sq. Feet

Primary Corridor of Window Breakage

Airborne Debris Area -- Mostly Collateral Damage

Scattered F-0 Damage to Oakland and I-30

Structure Units

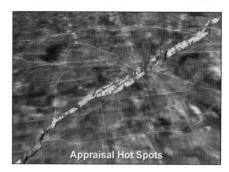

Appraisal Hot Spots

North Dallas "Hot Spot" with the Dollar Damage Risk Extruded in 3D Analyst

When a tornado devastated the suburbs of Oklahoma City in 1999, North Central Texas, less than 200 miles to the south and the most populated area in "tornado alley" took notice. Some clear questions emerged: How might the Dallas–Fort Worth area have fared under such an impact? Do recent tornado strikes in the Dallas–Fort Worth area represent the magnitude of risk that the region would face from a class of tornado like Oklahoma City? Long-track violent tornadoes are rare, but over time, many cities in tornado alley have experienced them and their devastating impact.

GIS helped assess the potential impact of such an event in the Dallas–Fort Worth area. Detailed damage mapping from Oklahoma City was merged with demographic, traffic, and developed data from North Central Texas to estimate the urban impacts from multiple scenario paths. The average urban paths produced damage estimates of about $2.5 billion with a few reaching more than $4 billion. The average path impacted 70,000 residents. Employees and vehicles in each path were also estimated.

Another assessment involved placing the damage contours of the Oklahoma City "Moore" F-5 tornado atop 50 different portions of North Central Texas. This tornado is a solid example of the long-tracked violent class tornadoes that have occurred on multiple occasions throughout Texas and the Midwest. Population and structure impacts are compared for each of these 50 paths. This task provides the best opportunity to look for trends in the Metroplex paths and to identify a possible "average" expectation for a storm of this magnitude. Evident in the data is a north Dallas hot spot. Seven damage paths in that area were modeled, which showed more than $3 billion of potential property damage. The area contained more than 25,000 individual structures and apartment units.

A study of a Fort Worth tornado strike in March 2002 revealed that this tornado was 135 times less powerful than the 1999 Oklahoma City tornado.

Tornado Damage Risk Assessment Estimating the Impact of a Big Outbreak to the Dallas–Fort Worth Metroplex
North Central Texas Council of Governments (NCTCOG)

Arlington, Texas, USA

By Scott W. Rae

Contact
Scott Rae, scott@dfwinfo.com

Software
ArcInfo, ArcView, ArcView Spatial Analyst, ArcView 3D Analyst, Microsoft Access, Microsoft PowerPoint, and Windows NT

Printer
HP DesignJet 1055C

Data Source(s)
NCTCOG, Dallas–Fort Worth area appraisal districts, National Severe Storms Laboratory, and National Weather Service

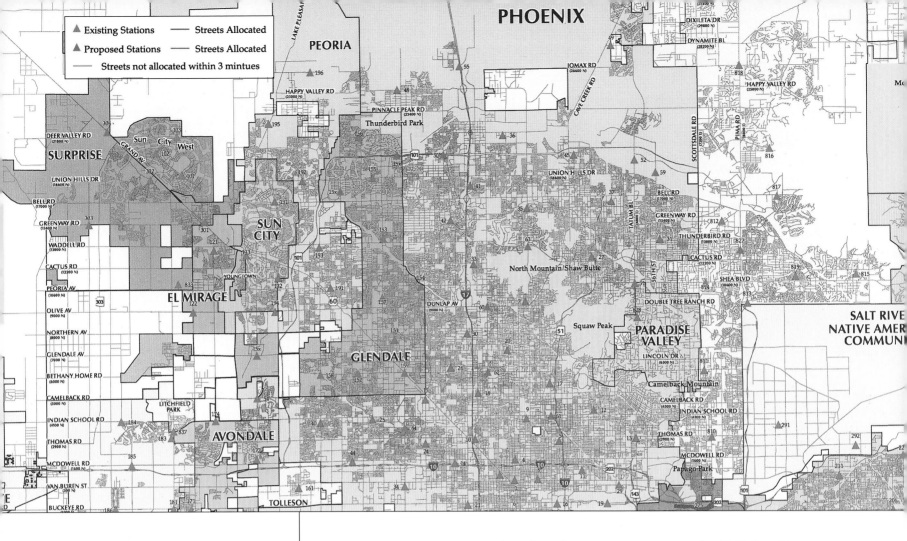

First Unit—Three-Minute Travel Time

City of Phoenix

Phoenix, Arizona, USA

By Dave Eaton

Contact

Dave Eaton, dave.eaton@phoenix.gov

Software

ArcInfo 8.0.1 and Solaris 2.6

Printer

HP DesignJet 1055CM

Data Source(s)

City of Phoenix

The City of Phoenix Fire Department facilitates fire and emergency management services (EMS) dispatching for 18 fire departments across the Valley of the Sun. The Phoenix Fire Department also works closely with bordering fire departments that maintain their own dispatching centers to provide the best possible customer service to the entire valley.

All agencies in the valley use the "automatic aid" approach to emergency responses, which in essence dissolves city political boundaries. This cooperative effort enables the fire departments to appear as one seamless department, which increases the level of service. A citizen in Phoenix might receive assistance from a fire apparatus from an adjacent city if that unit happens to be closer than a Phoenix unit. Most of the agencies across the valley use GPS technology for automatic vehicle location systems to provide continual apparatus locations even while they are traveling to ensure that the closest appropriate unit is dispatched. This equipment is directly related to a decrease in response times in emergencies.

To further decrease response times, allocation maps were created for the entire valley to help determine future station locations. Each existing or proposed station had streets allocated with the ArcNetwork module. Distance and speed limit impedance are the primary variables in creating the allocation.

This map displays the three-minute response areas for the first apparatus on scene across the valley. Streets allocated within three minutes to existing stations are shaded gray, while the streets allocated to proposed stations are shown in blue. The map also shows the areas that are outside the three-minute response area in red. The allocation model with the proposed stations included shows the increased level of service the valley will receive as additional stations are added.

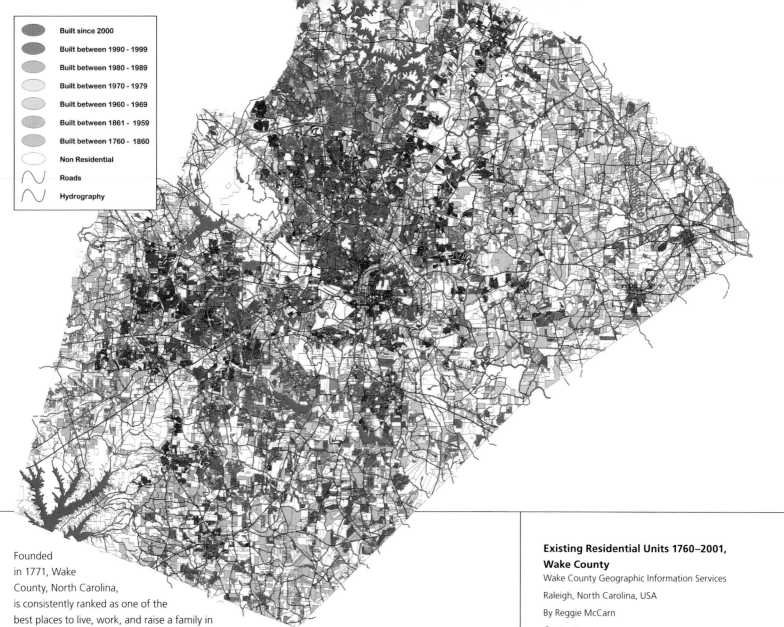

Built since 2000
Built between 1990 - 1999
Built between 1980 - 1989
Built between 1970 - 1979
Built between 1960 - 1969
Built between 1861 - 1959
Built between 1760 - 1860
Non Residential
Roads
Hydrography

Founded
in 1771, Wake
County, North Carolina,
is consistently ranked as one of the
best places to live, work, and raise a family in
the United States. Since 1990, there was a 47.3 percent
increase in population in the Raleigh–Durham–Research Triangle metropolitan area, and Wake County leaders wanted to know where the growth was occurring.

The map shown here is from a series produced for the county managers' growth management team. The map offered a new geographic perspective on what had suddenly become a high visibility issue in the second-largest populated county in North Carolina. Wake County commissioners have since created a Growth Management Task Force to develop a countywide consensus for growth management. GIS plays an important role in providing analysis and mapping products for projects dealing with growth management, watershed/water supply, land use, open space, and environmental initiatives.

Since the Wake County Geographic Information Services Department was formed in 1988, more than 150 layers of data have been automated for county departments and municipality use. Wake County GIS provides support to more than 200 users within county departments and agencies and to the 12 municipal governments within its boundaries. In addition to working with other City of Raleigh departments and contractors, the GIS Division shares close ties to the City of Raleigh GIS with joint application development and data sharing opportunities.

**Existing Residential Units 1760–2001,
Wake County**
Wake County Geographic Information Services
Raleigh, North Carolina, USA
By Reggie McCarn
Contact
Reggie McCarn, rmccarn@co.wake.nc.us
Software
ArcInfo 7.2, ArcView 3.2, and Windows NT
Printer
HP DesignJet 1055CM
Data Source(s)
Wake County GIS and Wake County Revenue

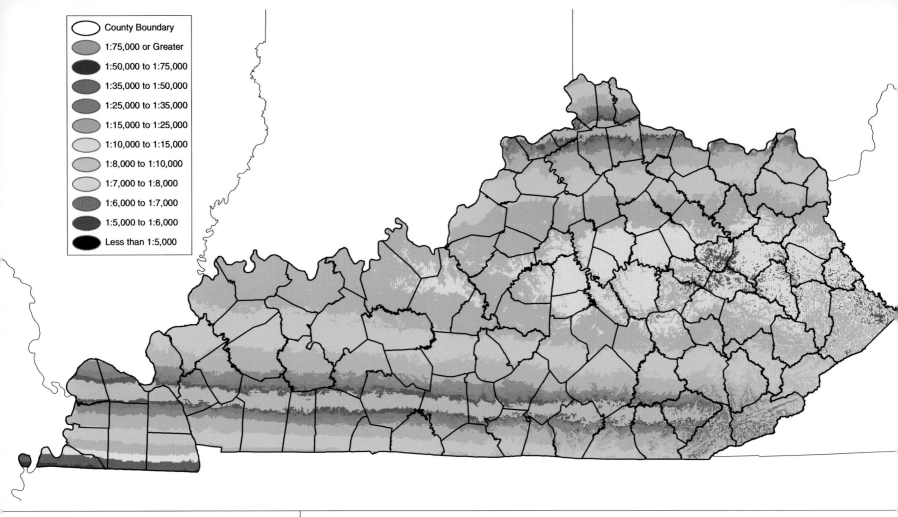

Legend:

- County Boundary
- 1:75,000 or Greater
- 1:50,000 to 1:75,000
- 1:35,000 to 1:50,000
- 1:25,000 to 1:35,000
- 1:15,000 to 1:25,000
- 1:10,000 to 1:15,000
- 1:8,000 to 1:10,000
- 1:7,000 to 1:8,000
- 1:6,000 to 1:7,000
- 1:5,000 to 1:6,000
- Less than 1:5,000

The Kentucky Single Zone State Plane Coordinate System

Kentucky Natural Resources and Environmental Protection Cabinet, Office of Information Services, Geographic Information Systems Branch

Frankfort, Kentucky, USA

By Bryan W. Bunch, PLS, PG

Contact
Bryan W. Bunch, bryan.bunch@mail.state.ky.us

Software
ArcMap 8.1, ArcToolbox™ 8.1, ArcPress, and AutoCAD Map 2000i

Hardware
Compaq DeskPro Pentium 4 workstation

Printer
HP DesignJet 3500CP

Data Source(s)
U.S. Geological Survey and Commonwealth of Kentucky

The State Plane coordinate system utilized by the United States was established in the 1930s to provide engineers and land surveyors with a way to georeference projects in standardized coordinate systems that could incorporate control monumentation established by the United States Coast and Geodetic Survey (National Geodetic Survey).

Analyzing raster and similar data sets on a statewide basis or over large geographic regions, such as watersheds or interstate highway corridors, is practical only when all data is presented in the same mapping projection or reference frame. Kentucky has approached this problem by developing the Kentucky Single Zone State Plane Coordinate System. This newly adopted projection was designed to cover the entire state in a balanced manner and attempts to minimize mapping distortions experienced between the ground and grid. The ultimate goal was to attain a mapping projection that met survey accuracy standards and could be utilized by the broadest range of mapping professionals including land surveyors and engineers. This was accomplished by determining worst-case ground to grid distortion ratios for all 7.5-minute topographic quadrangle maps covering Kentucky. The projection parameters were adjusted until a practical balance in overall mapping distortion was achieved that minimized extreme values as best as possible given the resolution of the data set.

This map presents a refinement of the original development approach resulting in a more accurate analysis of the final projection parameters. The higher resolution analysis indicates that the projection skews slightly to favor the north end of the state, which from a geopolitical perspective is commensurate with increased urbanization and higher property values of that area in comparison to the rural agricultural and forested southern end of the state. The greatest distortions are experienced at the southwestern portion of Kentucky and are due to the lowest elevations in the state occurring outside and farthest away from the southern standard parallel.

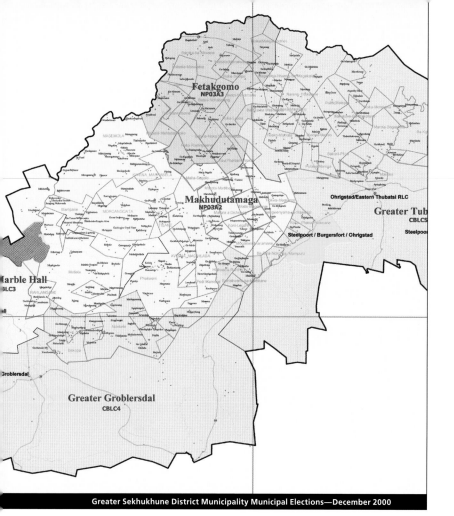

Greater Sekhukhune District Municipality Municipal Elections—December 2000

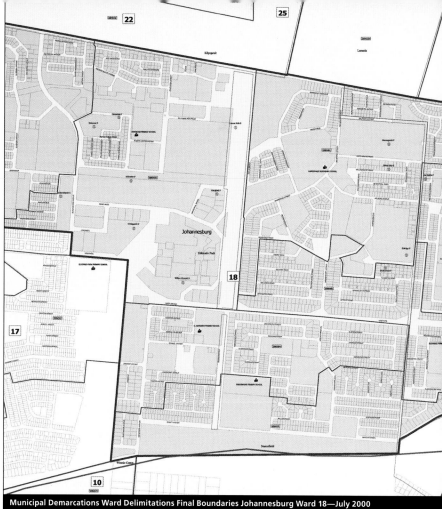

Municipal Demarcations Ward Delimitations Final Boundaries Johannesburg Ward 18—July 2000

During 1999 and 2000, all of South Africa's municipal boundaries were redemarcated in terms of the Municipal Demarcation Act. To promote the new boundaries, the Municipal Demarcation Board prepared a series of A0 maps of the entire country at the national, provincial, district, and local levels and A1 maps for each ward.

Greater Sekhukhune District Municipality Municipal Elections—December 2000

This is an example of a cross boundary district municipality map. The map shows the outer boundaries of the district municipality; the local municipalities; and other features such as roads, rivers, farm boundaries and names, and town names.

Municipal Demarcations Ward Delimitations Final Boundaries Johannesburg Ward 18—July 2000

This ward map is an extract of Ward 18 of the City of Johannesburg. The ward maps indicated the outer boundary of the ward, the voting districts that constituted the ward, and the location of the voting station as well as detailed cadastral data. In addition, other data sets were used to show the street names, suburb and village names, and location of institutions (schools, clinics, police stations). The map also gives the number of registered voters per voting district and the total number of voters in the ward.

The Municipal Demarcation Board produced and distributed maps to relevant organizations free of charge, and the series is well used. The board also created a GIS viewer called SA Explorer that was bundled with South Africa data sets and customized to enable users to search and retrieve spatial data easily. This viewer was distributed free of charge and placed third at ESRI's 2001 International User Conference in the MapObjects® Application category. Version 2 of the software is now available as well as an ArcIMS software-based mapping facility called SA Explorer Online. An online mapping service is available at www.demarcation.org.za. The board contracted the services of Data World (Pty.) Ltd. (www.dataworld.co.za) as its GIS consultant to undertake the mapping work.

Demarcation of Municipalities in South Africa for Elections 2000

Municipal Demarcation Board

Durban, South Africa

By Municipal Demarcation Board

Contact
Dr. Michael Sutcliffe, michael@demarcation.co.za

Software
ArcView 3.2 and Avenue™

Hardware
Pentium III PC

Printer
HP DesignJet 1050C

Data Source(s)
Municipal Demarcation Board, Surveyor General's Office, Statistics South Africa, Department of Education, Human Sciences Research Council, and Independent Elections Commission map

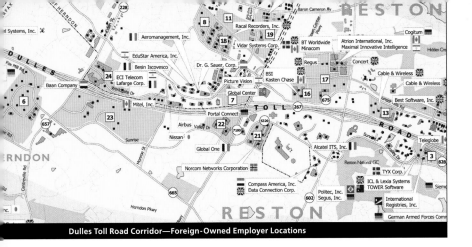

Dulles Toll Road Corridor—Foreign-Owned Employer Locations

Dulles Toll Road Corridor—Selected Employer Locations

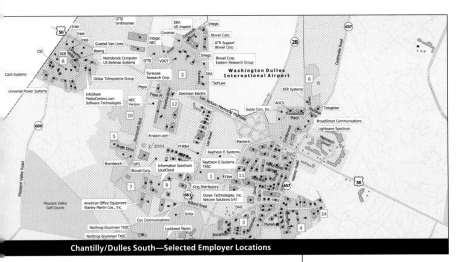

Chantilly/Dulles South—Selected Employer Locations

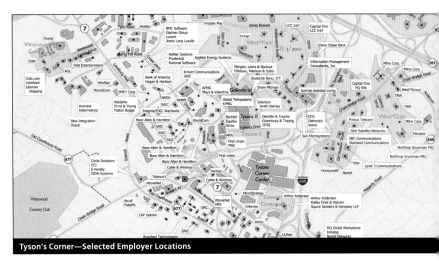

Tyson's Corner—Selected Employer Locations

Fairfax County Selected Employer Locations

Fairfax County Economic Development Authority (FCEDA)

Vienna, Virginia, USA

By Kevin Peterkin

Contact
Kevin Peterkin, kpeterkin@fceda.org

Software
ArcView 3.2a and Microsoft Access

Hardware
Dell OptiPlex GX1

Printer
Tektronix Phaser 740

Data Source(s)
FCEDA and Fairfax County

Fairfax County, Virginia, is located just outside of Washington, D.C., and is the largest jurisdiction in that region with nearly one million residents. During the last 40 years, the county has evolved from a sleepy bedroom community for the nation's capital into one of the premier suburban business centers in the country with nearly 100 million square feet of office space and more than 544,000 jobs. The Fairfax County Economic Development Authority (FCEDA) provides an array of free services and information to promote Fairfax County as a business location for domestic and foreign-owned companies and organizations.

This series of maps is produced by FCEDA to assist marketing managers in the promotion of Fairfax County as a world-class business location. These maps provide a visualization of the concentration and breadth of businesses located within three of the primary business centers in Fairfax County. In addition, a second series of maps depicts foreign-owned firms within these same business centers, and maps are available for other business centers in the county.

Initial work involved an inventory and survey of the county's commercial development, which totaled more than 2,800 office and industrial properties and more than 50 business parks. The properties were subsequently geocoded and the tables populated with relevant building information. This data is warehoused in a customized Microsoft Access database that affords easy integration into ArcView.

Fairfax County's Geographic Information Services and Mapping Branch supplies the rest of the information such as street centerlines, jurisdictions, cadastral information, airports, and parks. Standard fonts and symbols were used for the Selected Employer series, while flag symbols were imported for the Foreign-Owned Employer Locations map. These maps are updated quarterly.

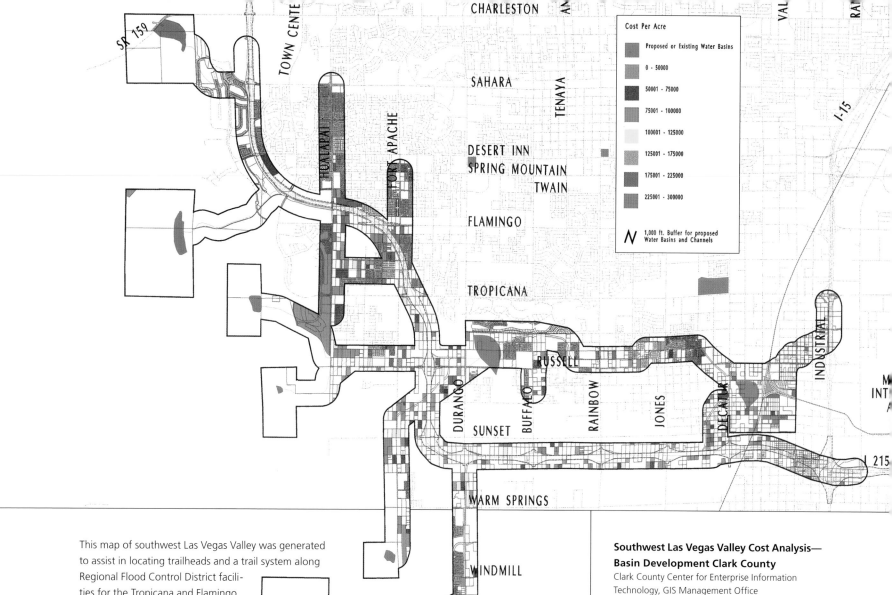

Cost Per Acre

Proposed or Existing Water Basins

0 – 50000

50001 – 75000

75001 – 100000

100001 – 125000

125001 – 175000

175001 – 225000

225001 – 300000

N 1,000 ft. Buffer for proposed
Water Basins and Channels

This map of southwest Las Vegas Valley was generated to assist in locating trailheads and a trail system along Regional Flood Control District facilities for the Tropicana and Flamingo Washes Recreation Plan.

The Clark County Trails Development program requested the cooperation of the U.S. Army Corps of Engineers, Regional Flood Control District, and Clark County Parks and Recreation in developing the Recreation Plan. Three trailheads and a park will be built in the Red Rock, Blue Diamond, Flamingo, and Tropicana Detention basins. In addition, a 20-mile trail system will be built to connect the trailheads to each other and to other trails being developed within this area of the valley.

The Water Resources Development Act of 1992 authorized and allowed for approximately $15 million in recreational improvements along these flood control facilities. The funding will be provided through federal grants and the Water Resources Development Act. This is a huge benefit for the citizens of and visitors to Clark County.

A Mylar map showing bike trails and parks in the area was produced as an overlay for this map.

Southwest Las Vegas Valley Cost Analysis—
Basin Development Clark County
Clark County Center for Enterprise Information Technology, GIS Management Office

Las Vegas, Nevada, USA

By Rose A. Broderick and Sharon Rice

Contact
Rose A. Broderick, rbr@co.clark.nv.us

Software
ArcInfo 7.0.2 and UNIX

Printer
HP DesignJet 1050

Data Source(s)
Clark County and Regional Flood Control District

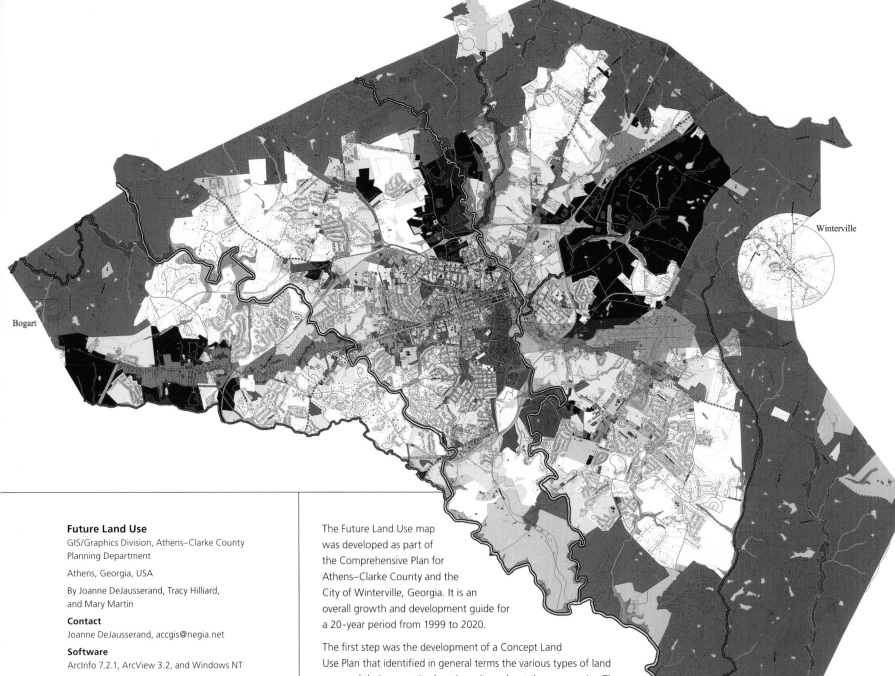

Winterville

Bogart

Future Land Use

GIS/Graphics Division, Athens–Clarke County Planning Department

Athens, Georgia, USA

By Joanne DeJausserand, Tracy Hilliard, and Mary Martin

Contact

Joanne DeJausserand, accgis@negia.net

Software

ArcInfo 7.2.1, ArcView 3.2, and Windows NT

Printer

HP DesignJet 750C

Data Source(s)

Athens–Clarke County GIS database

The Future Land Use map was developed as part of the Comprehensive Plan for Athens–Clarke County and the City of Winterville, Georgia. It is an overall growth and development guide for a 20-year period from 1999 to 2020.

The first step was the development of a Concept Land Use Plan that identified in general terms the various types of land uses and their respective locations throughout the community. The approved Concept Land Use Plan was used as the foundation for the creation of the parcel-specific Future Land Use map, which employs a series of more detailed land use classifications to organize the placement of various land uses throughout the county. Incorporated into this set of land use categories were several categories that have not been used before in Clarke County including three mixed-use categories—Community Mixed Use, Neighborhood Mixed Use, and Residential Mixed Use—that were intended to create a mixture of residential and commercial uses. A rural designation was designed to protect the agrarian and largely undeveloped portions of Clarke County.

The Future Land Use map is a legal document used in the planning process.

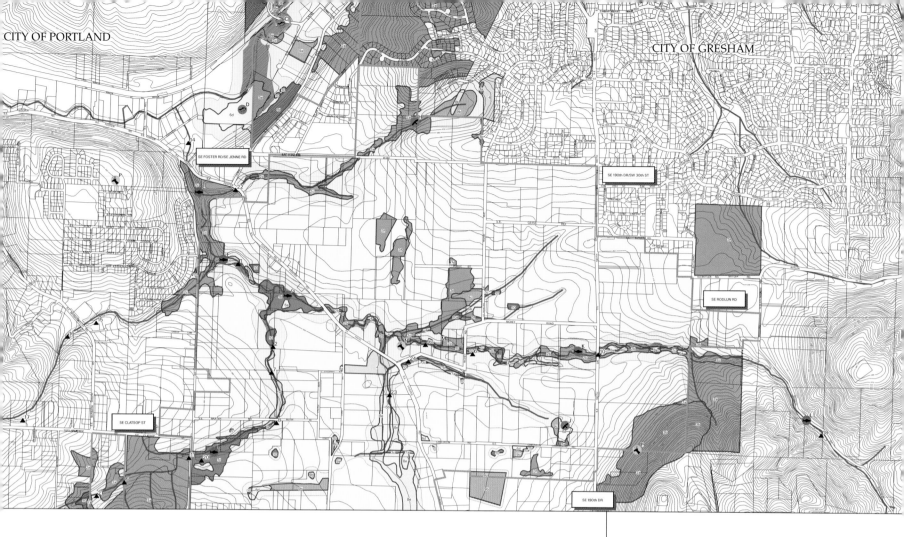

CITY OF PORTLAND

CITY OF GRESHAM

The purpose of this project is to create land use plans and policies for approximately 1,500 acres east of Portland and south of Gresham. Important elements of the Pleasant Valley Concept Plan include a land use plan for a combination of different types of housing and employment uses that support local and regional needs. The land use plan is expected to include a town center to create opportunities for residents to work and conduct business near their homes.

Another expectation of the planning process is natural resource and watershed protection with planned strategies to minimize the impact from transportation and development such as strategically located parks and open spaces, managed water crossings, limited impervious surfaces, and restoration of habitat.

The transportation plan will serve the needs of the expected community by providing a variety of travel choices that maximize accessibility to nearby regional centers, transit corridors, and employment centers within the area.

The project is a joint planning effort among the cities of Gresham, Portland, and Happy Valley; Clackamas and Multnomah counties; and Metro, the regional government. It is funded by a Federal Highway Administration grant. A team of consultants led by OTAK, Inc., is assisting in this project.

Pleasant Valley Resource Management Map
Metro Data Resource Center

Portland, Oregon, USA

By Laura Freeman, Metro Data Resource Center; and Justin Healy, OTAK, Inc.

Contact
Laura Freeman, freemanl@metro.dst.or.us

Software
ArcView 3.2 and Windows NT

Printer
HP DesignJet 2500

Data Source(s)
Metro Data Resource Center; OTAK, Inc.; U.S. Geological Survey; Oregon Department of Fish and Wildlife Portland Bureau of Environmental Service; and Adolfson Associates, Inc.

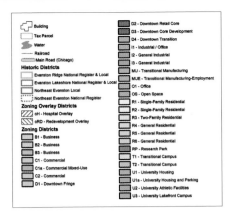

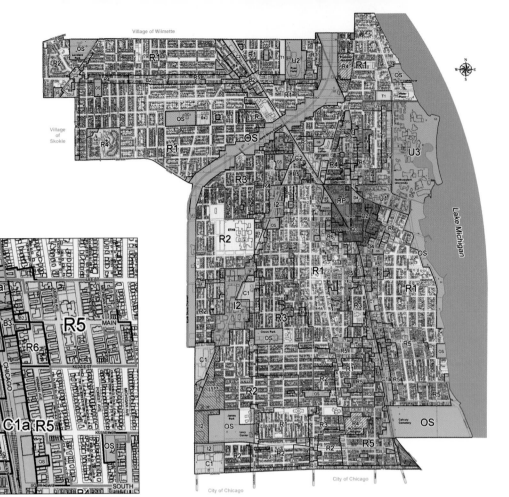

City of Evanston Zoning

City of Evanston

Evanston, Illinois, USA

By Pat Keegan, Marc Mylott, and Mark Varner

Contact
Pat Keegan, pkeegan@cityofevanston.org

Software
ArcInfo 8.1, ArcSDE™ 8.1, Oracle 8.1.7, Microsoft Excel, Microsoft Word, and Windows 2000

Hardware
Dell Precision 420 Pentium III workstation

Printer
HP DesignJet 755CM

Data Source(s)
City of Evanston GIS

Founded in 1863, Evanston is located immediately north of Chicago along Lake Michigan with a thriving, diverse community of just under 75,000 people within roughly eight square miles.

To regulate the use and development intensity of land, Evanston employs 30 zoning districts, two overlay districts, and four historic districts. Since 1921, when land within the city was first placed into one of five districts, the city has relied on black-and-white, hand-drawn maps to display this important information. Today, Evanston's GIS provides many advantages. Boundaries are more precise, color communicates a hierarchy of land use, and map updates and the production of a new map take a fraction of the time. This map is an official document of the Zoning Ordinance of the City of Evanston.

The Zoning map is used by a number of people in a number of ways. Residents may use the map as a starting point to determine whether a proposed addition to their home meets city code. Developers use the map to evaluate the development potential of parcels they may be interested in acquiring. City staff use the map to evaluate the impact of policy decisions at the local, neighborhood, and citywide levels.

The Zoning map is available in several formats including 26" x 26" plots, 36" x 36" plots, and PDF downloads from the city's Web site. In addition, an ArcIMS application provides an interactive map utilizing similar layers and symbology. The Zoning map contains more than 12 geographic layers completely maintained by the GIS Division and stored as ArcSDE feature classes including tax parcels, building footprints, wards, historic districts, and various annotation layers. It represents a collaborative effort between the GIS Division and the Zoning Division. The Evanston GIS Division supports all other city departments with data, maps, Web applications, and geographic analysis.

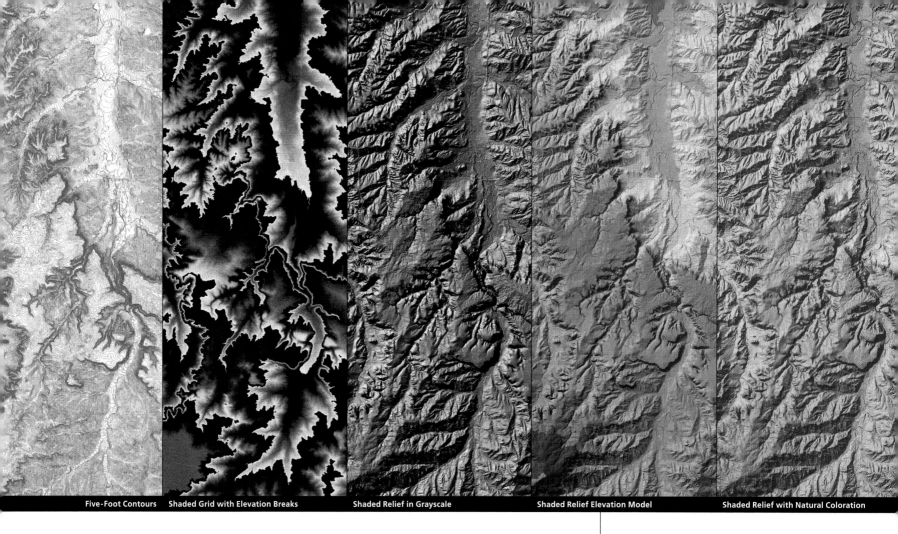

Five-Foot Contours **Shaded Grid with Elevation Breaks** **Shaded Relief in Grayscale** **Shaded Relief Elevation Model** **Shaded Relief with Natural Coloration**

The topographic elements presented here represent a sampling of what the Town of Castle Rock has used to analyze its surroundings.

These data sets have helped establish base elevations for water tanks as well as identify elevation ranges for water pressure zones. Detailed analysis of the data has revealed hydrologic features and watershed drainage patterns.

This data has also been used to determine sensitive areas in ridgeline and skyline preservation analyses, and the information was used to enact ordinances to protect those sensitive areas.

Aside from the planimetric data that is used regularly, the topographic data sets would be considered the most valuable data at Castle Rock.

Topography of the Town of Castle Rock
Town of Castle Rock

Castle Rock, Colorado, USA

By Joel A. Alexander

Contact
Joel A. Alexander, jalexander@ci.castlerock.co.us

Software
ArcInfo 8.0.1 and Windows NT

Printer
HP DesignJet 1050C

Data Source(s)
Town of Castle Rock

〰️ State Route	▬▬▬ Expressway	
🔲 US Highway	▬▬ Major Arterial	
🔲 Interstate	── Minor Arterial	
110 Exit Number	── Collector Street	
F Fire Station	⋯ Local Street	
F Future Fire Station	─ ─ Proposed Minor Arterial	
69 Government Facility	⋯⋯ Council District Boundary	
⚑ Public School Facility	⋯⋯ Urban Service Area Boundary	
⛳ Public Golf Course	─·─ County Boundary	
H Hospital	┼┼┼ Railroad	
Civic Center	⋯ Creek	
UK University of Kentucky	▓ Waterbody	
Transylvania University	░ Park	
Council District Number		
13 Location Number		

INDEX NOTES:
* Denotes feature that is outside the map extent.
Indexes apply to both sides of the map.

Map of Lexington–Fayette County

Lexington–Fayette Urban County Government
Geographic Information Services (LFUCG GIS)

Lexington, Kentucky, USA

By Tom Moreland and Phillip Stiefel

Contact
Phillip Stiefel, phillips@lfucg.com

Software
ArcInfo, ArcView 3.2, Adobe PageMaker,
Macromedia Freehand, and Windows NT

Printer
Off-site printer (Host Printing)

Data Source(s)
LFUCG GIS

This overview or index map of Lexington, Kentucky, was produced in conjunction with the development of an atlas of Lexington. The atlas included this 39-inch by 26-inch map as an insert. The map grid corresponds with the page numbers of the atlas and is synchronized by using the same symbology, data layers, and site indexes.

The map was produced using ArcView 3.2. The data is accessed via ArcInfo library coverages and exported into PostScript to a commercial printing facility. The printer used Freehand and PageMaker software to translate the image for prepress and into the final printing format. All source data is collected, verified, and maintained by the GIS Section of the Urban County government, either in the field using a global positioning system or in-house via historical research and/or visual verification using aerial images.

More than 5,000 copies were produced. Maps and atlases are available to all government employees and are sold to the public at cost.

Generalized Digital Reference Map

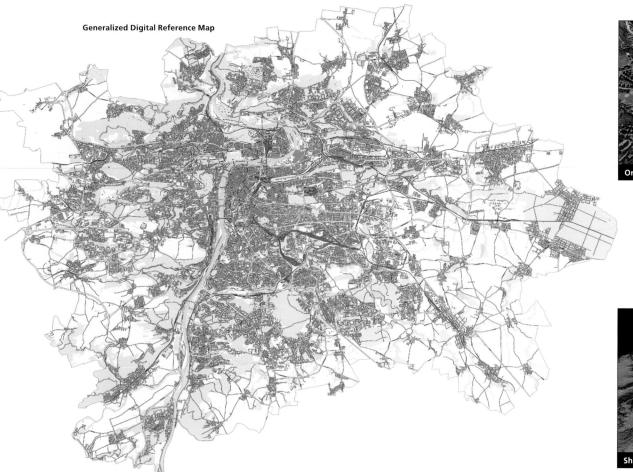

Orthophoto with Buildings

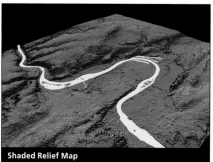

Shaded Relief Map

The Digital Reference Maps (DRM) are a set of digital maps of Prague that integrates graphical and alpha-numerical data into a comprehensive system. Prague, the capital of the Czech Republic, covers more than 496 square kilometers and consists of 112 cadastral areas and approximately 300,000 parcels, 230,000 buildings, 110,000 addresses, and 36,000 street sections.

The DRM comprise 30 layers that can be combined. The main layers consist of parcels, lines inside parcels, block maps (blocks of land use), addresses, buildings, street sections, and a generalized map. Layers for the cadastral map are kept in two forms—the "real" and the "law"—because of the many ownership changes after 1989. This has created a time lag in updating maps at the Cadastral Authority. In the "real" state, there are objects that best reflect the factual situation although they have not been authorized by the Cadastral Authority.

In addition to the main layers, there are other layers such as orthophotos, several sheet line systems, cadastral and municipal borders, and utilities. Most of the layers of DRM were created in 1993 by scanning and digitizing the 1:1,000-scale cadastral map and the 1:500-scale technical map and joining databases from the Cadastral Authority and the address database.

Since 1995, the maps have been updated from geodetic measurements and aerial orthophotos for better accuracy. The present positional accuracy of more than 80 percent of the objects is better than ±14 centimeters. Data is available in ArcInfo coverages and accessible in ArcView shapefiles and some other formats.

The DRM can be used as a base for other GIS applications or for cartographic purposes. There are many users among local government, utility managers, schools, and private companies.

Digital Reference Maps of Capital Prague
IMIP PRAHA

Prague, Czech Republic

By Ingrid Nosková

Contact
Ingrid Nosková, noskovai@imip.mepnet.cz

Software
ArcInfo 8.0.2, ArcView 3.2, ArcView 3D Analyst, and Windows NT

Printer
HP DesignJet 5000PS

Data Source(s)
Institute of Municipal Informatics of Capital Prague

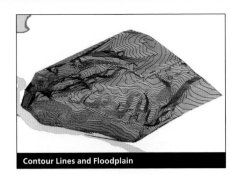

Contour Lines and Floodplain

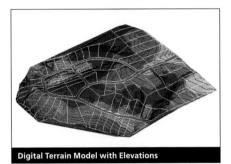

Digital Terrain Model with Elevations

Percent Slope of Property

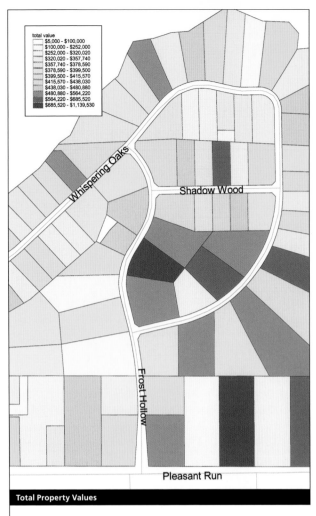

total value

	$5,000 - $100,000
	$100,000 - $252,000
	$252,000 - $320,020
	$320,020 - $357,740
	$357,740 - $378,590
	$378,590 - $399,500
	$399,500 - $415,570
	$415,570 - $438,030
	$438,030 - $480,880
	$480,880 - $564,220
	$564,220 - $685,520
	$685,520 - $1,139,530

Total Property Values

0.5-Meter Resolution, 1-Meter Horizontal Accuracy

Dallas Central Appraisal District Maps

Dallas Central Appraisal District

Dallas, Texas, USA

By Robert Lee Hoffpauer and Paul Lauder

Contact
Robert Lee Hoffpauer, hoff@dcad.org

Software
ArcView 3.2 and Windows NT 4.0

Printer
HP DesignJet 5000PS

Data Source(s)
In-house

Nearing completion, the Dallas Central Appraisal District's GIS includes digital orthophotography, parcels, and elevations. Using just these elements (there are others) and the tabular appraisal data, an appraiser can perform analyses ranging from routine to sophisticated—from thematic shading by attribute values to usability (slope) or viewshed (can this property see the lake?).

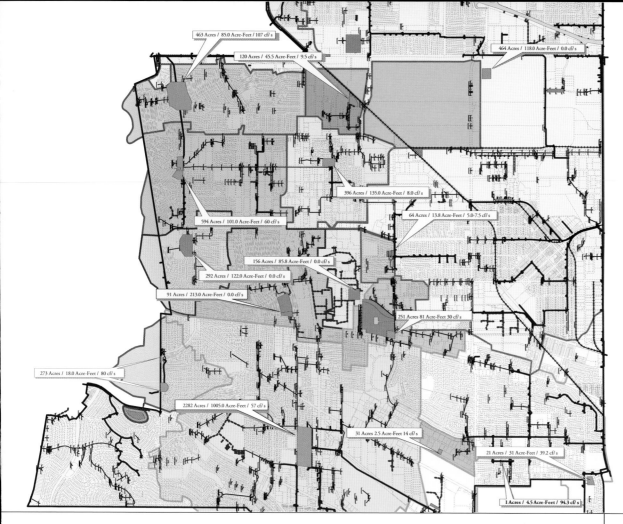

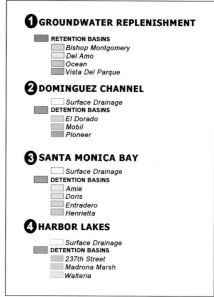

Four Ultimate Receiving Waters of Torrance Storm Drainage

City of Torrance Engineering Department

Torrance, California, USA

By Bruce Bornemann, Jenny Gough, and Larry Jenno

Contact
Jenny Gough, jgough@torrnet.com

Software
ArcView 3.2a, ArcPress, and Windows NT

Hardware
Dell workstation

Printer
HP DesignJet 755CM

Data Source(s)
City of Torrance

Torrance is situated approximately 15 miles southwest of Los Angeles. Located on a coastal plain area in Southern California, this 21-square-mile city is home to approximately 138,000 people.

This map graphically represents the final destination of storm water routed through Torrance. Sixty percent of the Torrance watershed areas drain directly to the receiving waters, with the remaining 40 percent draining to holding basins. Torrance is atypical in having four storm water retention basins (shown in blue) that directly filter the water runoff and assist in groundwater recharging. Storm water runoff that collects in those areas of Torrance that do not drain to retention basins is accumulated in detention basins (shown in green) before being pumped out toward Los Angeles Harbor or Santa Monica Bay.

As authorized by the Clean Water Act, the National Pollutant Discharge Elimination System permit program controls water pollution by regulating point sources that discharge pollutants into waters of the United States. These new regulations require Torrance to work upstream along the drainage system to identify potential problems and to monitor the quality of storm water runoff from point sources. This map helps the city to meet the new regulatory requirements by providing asset management information and an overview of the flows to the four ultimate receiving waters for Torrance.

Other companion GIS data not shown on this map will assist in the cleanup work. A completed storm drain modeling package will give near design-level performance indicators for each storm drainage facility in the city. In addition to providing a capital improvement program for the drainage system, these indicators will direct resource application for runoff cleanup work to the areas of highest need. Performance indicators will also facilitate automatic sizing and estimating of the new cleanup facilities.

Richard W. Burtt
Engineering Director
City of Torrance, California

City of Torrance Engineering Department

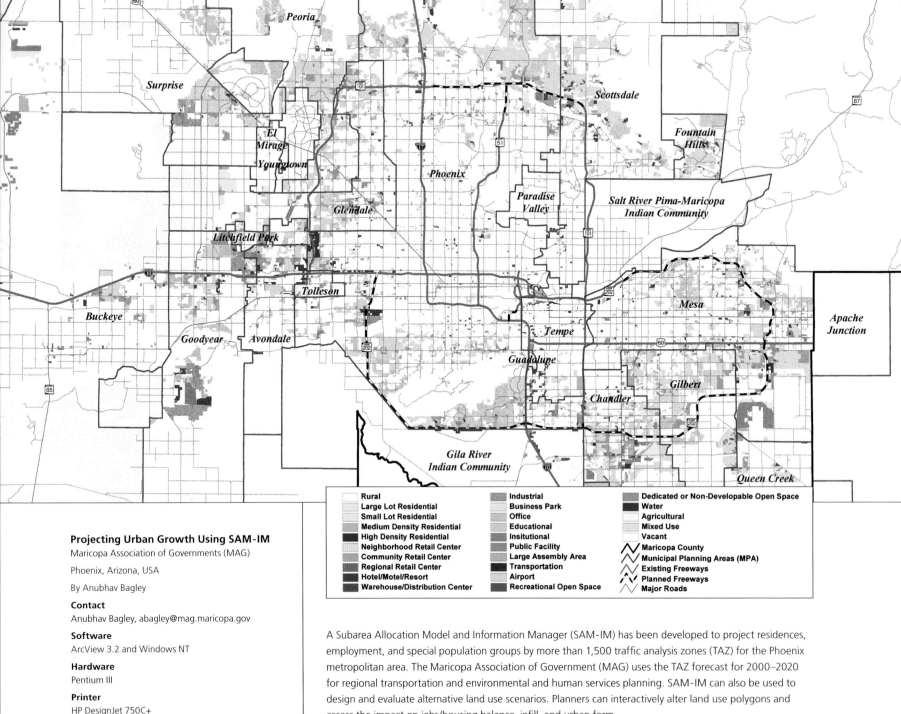

☐	Rural	☐	Industrial	☐	Dedicated or Non-Developable Open Space
☐	Large Lot Residential	☐	Business Park	☐	Water
☐	Small Lot Residential	☐	Office	☐	Agricultural
☐	Medium Density Residential	☐	Educational	☐	Mixed Use
☐	High Density Residential	☐	Insitutional	☐	Vacant
☐	Neighborhood Retail Center	☐	Public Facility	⌁	Maricopa County
☐	Community Retail Center	☐	Large Assembly Area	⌁	Municipal Planning Areas (MPA)
☐	Regional Retail Center	☐	Transportation	⌁	Existing Freeways
☐	Hotel/Motel/Resort	☐	Airport	⌁	Planned Freeways
☐	Warehouse/Distribution Center	☐	Recreational Open Space	⌁	Major Roads

Projecting Urban Growth Using SAM-IM

Maricopa Association of Governments (MAG)

Phoenix, Arizona, USA

By Anubhav Bagley

Contact
Anubhav Bagley, abagley@mag.maricopa.gov

Software
ArcView 3.2 and Windows NT

Hardware
Pentium III

Printer
HP DesignJet 750C+

Data Source(s)
MAG, Arizona Department of Economic Security, and Maricopa County Flood Control District

A Subarea Allocation Model and Information Manager (SAM-IM) has been developed to project residences, employment, and special population groups by more than 1,500 traffic analysis zones (TAZ) for the Phoenix metropolitan area. The Maricopa Association of Government (MAG) uses the TAZ forecast for 2000–2020 for regional transportation and environmental and human services planning. SAM-IM can also be used to design and evaluate alternative land use scenarios. Planners can interactively alter land use polygons and assess the impact on jobs/housing balance, infill, and urban form.

SAM-IM predicts future growth and urbanization by simulating development. The allocation mechanism evaluates the suitability of land to absorb development and chooses the most appropriate sites in conformance with general plans and development constraints. Data from the 2000 U.S. census and MAG's local GIS and database collection and review process will be used by SAM-IM to prepare the next set of TAZ projections for the MAG region during 2002.

This map displays land use changes as modeled by SAM-IM for a test scenario for population and employment growth between 2000 and 2040 in the Phoenix metropolitan area.

Maricopa Association of Governments

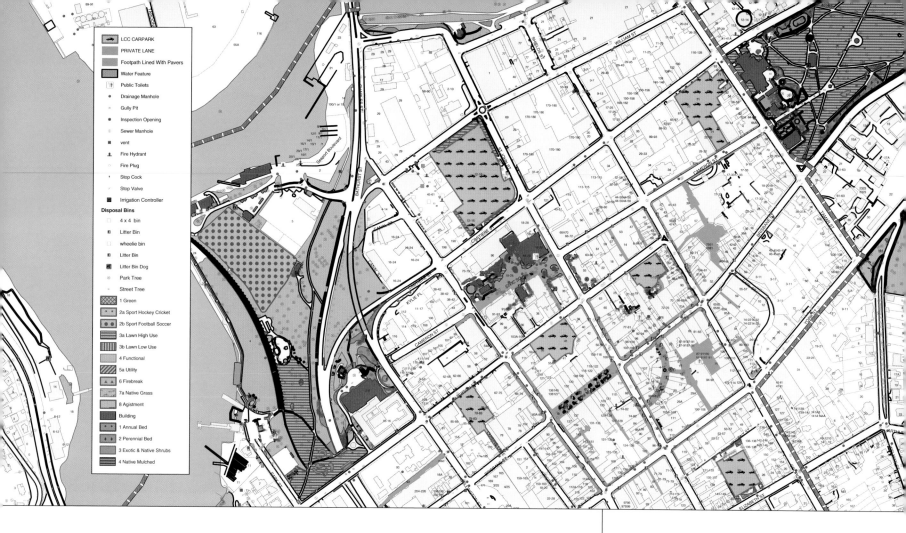

The municipality of Launceston covers an area of approximately 1,400 square kilometers and serves an urban and rural population of 98,000. Launceston City Council is responsible for the maintenance of 700 kilometers of urban and rural roads, 580 kilometers of footpaths, 1,000 kilometers of sewer and storm water pipelines, 520 kilometers of water reticulation, and more than 1,300 hectares of bushland and parkland within the municipality.

GIS is used extensively within the council to assist in management and future planning within the municipality. The Central City Maintenance map is a simple example of how the council uses GIS.

To assist in the maintenance of public assets, the council is in the process of developing a series of major service specifications. They will outline a range of minimum requirements for the upkeep of council assets and will cover the maintenance of public toilets, car parks, signage, parklands, gully pits, valves and hydrants, litter bins, and roads. The Central City Maintenance Area specification is the first of these.

The Central City Maintenance Area map covers an area of 1.03 square kilometers centered on the Launceston central business district. Created using ArcGIS 8.1, the map was generated from more than 30 layers by ArcSDE 8.1 on an Oracle platform. A range of predefined and customized symbology is used to represent the parking lots, parks, sporting grounds, street and park trees, gully pits, and disposal bins among other assets. The map accompanies the specification documentation to assist both the council and the service provider.

Central City Maintenance Area
Launceston City Council

Launceston, Tasmania, Australia

By Adrian Large, Steven Millett, Chris Moore, Fred Schoenmaker, and Julian Ward

Contact
Hector Beveridge, hector.beveridge@launceston.tas.gov.au

Software
ArcGIS 8.1, ArcSDE, and Windows NT

Printer
HP DesignJet 1055CM

Data Source(s)
Council corporate data sets

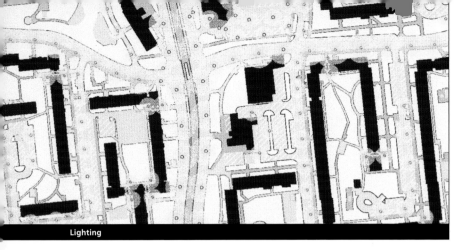

Lighting

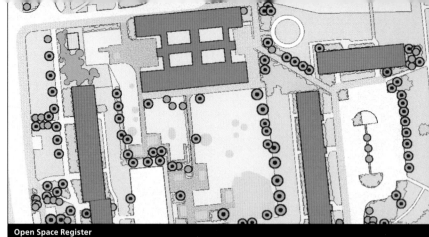

Open Space Register

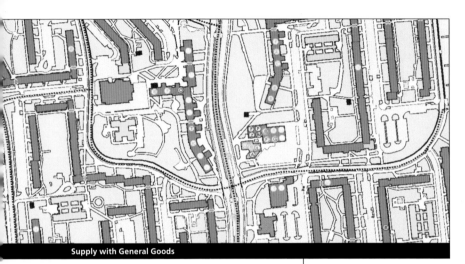

Supply with General Goods

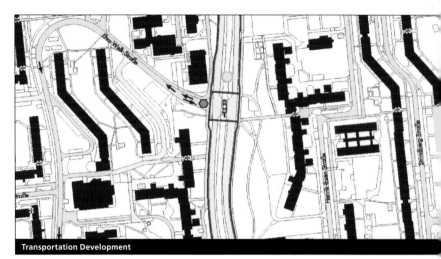

Transportation Development

Integrated Urban Development

Planungsbüro für Ingenieurbauwerke und
Verkehrsanlagen GmbH (PLANIVER)

Neubrandenburg, Germany

By Thomas Weber and Stefan Höse

Contact
Thomas Weber, tweber@planiver.de

Software
ArcView 3.1, ArcPress, Corel Draw, and Windows NT

Hardware
Pentium III

Printer
HP DesignJet 1050

Data Source(s)
Land surveys, aerial photography, and city maps

The urban planning department of Rostock is using an urban information system to characterize its state of development and determine potential planning sites, wasteland, and problem sites.

The four maps are a part of a larger process involved in using a GIS to develop an urban quarter. They are used as layers to form larger main categories or data blocks including land use, open space, transportation, and social infrastructure.

The GIS-based analysis has played an essential role for the city in setting goals and developing strategic plans for a problematic urban corridor. In addition, the information can be continuously updated for further land use management policies.

POTENTIAL SLIDE AREA	$\sim$	DWU INDEX BOUNDARY	$\sim$	COMBINED MAINLINE	$\sim$	CULVERT	⚫	WORK ACTIVITY 407, ACTKEY 1008 WITH WO-ID
STEEP SLOPE AREA	$\sim$	SEWER MAINLINE	$\sim$	METRO MAINLINE	○	MAINTENANCE HOLE		
KNOWN SLIDE AREA	$\sim$	DRAINAGE MAINLINE	$\sim$	ABANDONED PIPE				
RIGHT OF WAY			$\sim$	DITCH	$\sim$	Seattle City Limit		BLACK TEXT DENOTES MAINTENANCE HOLE ID

Infrastructure Repairs in Slide-Sensitive Areas—Work Activity 407

Seattle Public Utilities

Seattle, Washington, USA

By Kamol Yesuwan

Contact
Kamol Yesuwan, kamol.yesuwan@ci.seattle.wa.us

Software
ArcInfo 8.0.1 and UNIX

Hardware
Sun Ultra 10 workstation

Printer
HP DesignJet 1055CM

Data Source(s)
City of Seattle

Seattle has developed a program of closed circuit television (CCTV) inspection for sewer and drainage main lines in areas that are prone to landslide, have experienced landslides, or have steep slopes. Structural deficiencies are identified and prioritized for repair through the CCTV inspection program.

Work Activity 407 represents repairs performed by Seattle staff on sewer or drainage main lines. Identifying the location of infrastructure in these sensitive areas is critical to the work activity. Because the areas are more sensitive, scheduling repairs requires more planning. For example, soils specialists evaluate soil conditions to ensure appropriate measures are taken to keep the slopes stable. In addition, timing of the repair may be more critical if the structural deficiency contributes to groundwater or if infiltration is prevalent because those conditions could possibly contribute to accelerated deterioration of the pipe and/or instability of the slope.

Tasmania 1:25,000 Series—Leventhorpe

Department of Primary Industries,
Water and Environment

Tasmania, Australia

By Bruce Graham and Max Neil

Contact
Stuart Fletcher, Stuart.Fletcher@dpiwe.tas.gov.au

Software
ArcInfo 8.1

Hardware
IBM RS/6000 workstation

Printer
Linotype-HELL 3030 and HP DesignJet 5000PS

Data Source(s)
Land Information System Tasmania databases

The 1:25,000 map series was produced for more than 20 years by traditional cartographic methods. In 1996, the Department of Primary Industries, Water and Environment investigated automated methods of map production for the map series. It was decided that ArcInfo using a custom application was the best solution.

This application uses ArcEdit™, and ArcPlot™ edits and plots map tiles with a minimum of input from users. The application enables users to place text, edit feature attributes, and change feature symbology while in the editing environment. When editing on the map tile is complete, the automated plotting routines can generate a map composition. Map compositions are output for quality assurance using an HP DesignJet 5000PS and then the map is color separated and output as PostScript files. The PostScript files are plotted on a Linotype-HELL 3030 as CMYK film plates for Cromalin proofing and final printing.

This method of map production has reduced compilation time for maps to approximately 25 percent of the time previously spent using traditional methods and has significantly reduced the costs. To date, approximately 30 maps out of the 400 map series have been produced using these automated methods. The 1:25,000 series is nearing complete coverage of the state and during the next few years will undergo significant revision.

The entire map series can be viewed through the Land Information System Tasmania (LIST) Web site at www.thelist.tas.gov.au.

Department of Primary Industries, Water and Environment

In 2001, the New Berlin assessor asked the Land Information Services Division to create new assessor's maps. These maps are used as a base map for the assessment of property. The maps that they were using were old and worn. Essentially, the original base map had not changed since 1971. For the past 30 years, lot splits, combinations, and subdivisions were drawn in pencil or plats were copied and taped onto the map.

Land Information Services created new assessor's maps using ArcView 3.2. These maps consist of three views, the quarter section window, address grid, and index map. The quarter section window contains 72 themes such as parcel lines, road rights-of-way, extended lot lines, subdivision boundaries, building footprints, schools, easements, and associated annotation. The city assessor found the new colored maps much easier to use. In addition, Land Information Services can easily print out a new sheet whenever a major change takes place.

To prevent having to create 147 different layouts (one for each quarter section in the city), Land Information Services wrote an Avenue script that would automatically adjust the view extent and relevant layout text and highlight the appropriate area on the index map.

City of New Berlin Assessor's Map
City of New Berlin
New Berlin, Wisconsin, USA
By David B. Haines

Contact
David Haines, dhaines@newberlin.org

Software
ArcView 3.2, Avenue, and Windows

Hardware
Intel workstation

Printer
HP DesignJet 1055CM

Data Source(s)
City of New Berlin Department of Community
Development and Waukesha County

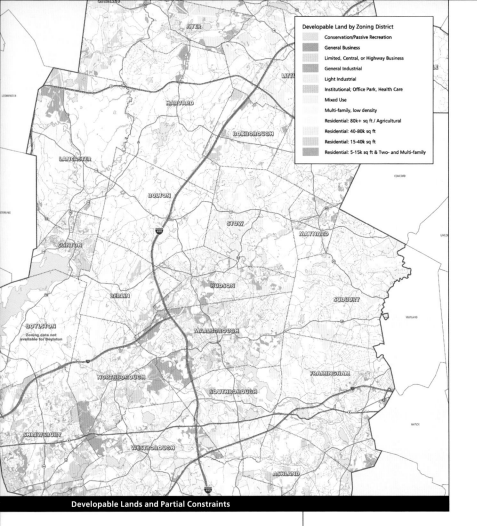

Developable Lands and Partial Constraints

Absolute Development Constraints

Development Constraints—
Interstate 495 Region

Massachusetts Geographic Information System (MassGIS) Commonwealth of Massachusetts

Boston, Massachusetts, USA

By Michael Trust

Contact
Michael Trust, michael.trust@state.ma.us

Software
ArcView 3.2a and Windows NT 4.0

Printer
HP DesignJet 2500CP

Data Source(s)
MassGIS and Massachusetts regional planning agencies

As part of its Community Preservation Initiative, the state Executive Office of Environmental Affairs (EOEA) contracted with the 13 Massachusetts regional planning agencies (RPA) and consultants to provide a build-out map and analysis of all 351 cities and towns in the commonwealth. A build-out analysis is a series of GIS-based maps that illustrate a community's current zoning, the land available for development and how it is zoned, and maximum development possible in a particular community if every piece of developable land was developed based on existing local zoning. Accompanying the maps are projections of the numbers of residents, households, public school students, and water use at build out. The analysis is a planning tool that demonstrates development as it could occur if no changes are made to current zoning, and it helps to stimulate discussion as communities continue to grow. EOEA's watershed team leaders and RPA presented each city or town's build-out analysis to city councils and boards of selectmen in all 351 communities.

Absolute Development Constraints—Interstate 495 Region is the first in the set of maps for a super summit held in May 2001 for 27 communities in the Interstate 495 beltway. It displays land already developed or absolutely constrained. Such constraints may vary from town to town due to zoning regulations but generally include steep slopes, wetlands, and floodplains. Current regionalized zoning codes, protected open space, and recent subdivisions are featured.

Developable Lands and Partial Constraints—Interstate 495 Region is the second in the set of super summit maps. It displays land potentially developable, symbolized by a regional zoning classification. Massachusetts Geographic Information System derived these regional zoning codes to assure a standard legend across a state in which the 351 communities' zoning codes vary greatly. For more information on the methodology used in the build-out analyses, visit www.state.ma.us/mgis/buildout.htm.

Massachusetts Geographic Information System

Land Use, 1951

Land Use, 1999

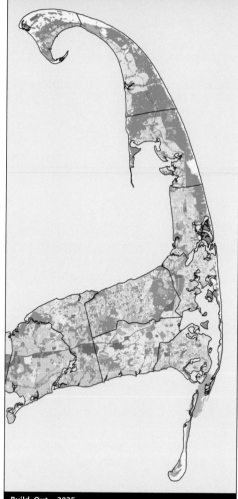

Build-Out, ~2025

The Cape Cod region in Massachusetts has comprehensive historical land use data spanning a period of approximately 50 years. The information can be used to create a time series of snapshots that can be analyzed for change patterns.

In this series, land use information was collected for the years 1951 to 1971, 1985, 1990, and 1999. An aggregate classification was used to represent the major types of land uses customarily found on Cape Cod. It was designated around relationships observed between the MacConnell land use classification scheme and the regionalized zoning code scheme presently in use by the Massachusetts Geographic Information System. By relating existing land use with zoning (potential land use), it is possible to build a model and make predictions about future land use trends.

A trend of development is apparent in this time series. Initially, those areas along the immediate coastline were most densely developed. Since then, a steady migration of development inland has occurred. Higher-density residential areas have flourished, primarily at the cost of natural vegetated lands. Furthermore, the increased infrastructure (major roads) has attracted even higher-density uses, especially those dedicated to commercial uses. Today, almost half of the land on Cape Cod can be classified as developed.

Cape Cod Development Time Series, 1951–1999

Massachusetts Geographic Information System (MassGIS) Commonwealth of Massachusetts

Boston, Massachusetts, USA

By Daniel Marrier

Contact
Daniel Marrier, daniel.marrier@state.ma.us

Software
ArcView 3.2a and Windows NT 4.0

Printer
HP DesignJet 2500CP

Data Source(s)
MassGIS

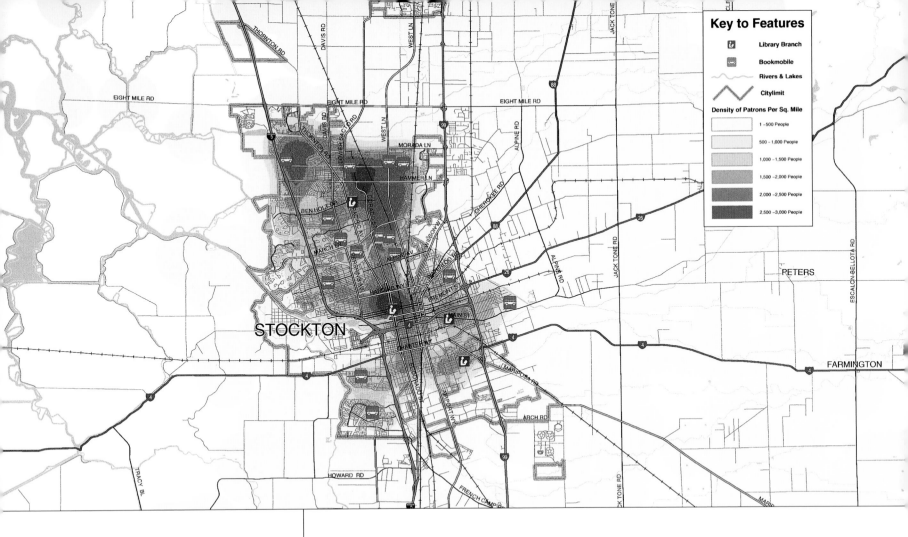

Library Patron Density in
San Joaquin County

City of Stockton, Administrative Services Department,
Management Information Services Division

Stockton, California, USA

By Robert MacLeod

Contact
Robert MacLeod, robert.macleod@ci.stockton.ca.us

Software
ArcInfo, ArcGIS Spatial Analyst, and Windows NT

Hardware
IBM AIX server

Printer
HP DesignJet 1055CM

Data Source(s)
City of Stockton GIS, Stockton–San Joaquin County
Public Library, and San Joaquin County Community
Development Department GIS

This map was one of many maps produced to analyze the spatial relationship between library users and existing library facilities. The mapping process involved querying for all active library users from the library's patron database. The addresses from these patron records were geocoded to a street centerline coverage to create point locations. ArcGIS Spatial Analyst was used to create density surfaces from the geocoded patron address records.

The library used the map to show how the library users are dispersed throughout the county. Within each county community, the map helps identify potential future branch locations and/or bookmobile stops to provide ready access to patrons who may not be using the existing branches due to inconvenient location. A recently passed proposition by the voters of California made $350 million available in bond money for the construction of public libraries. The maps gave the library managers a graphic demonstration of the gaps in library facilities and aided in the application process for four new branch facilities.

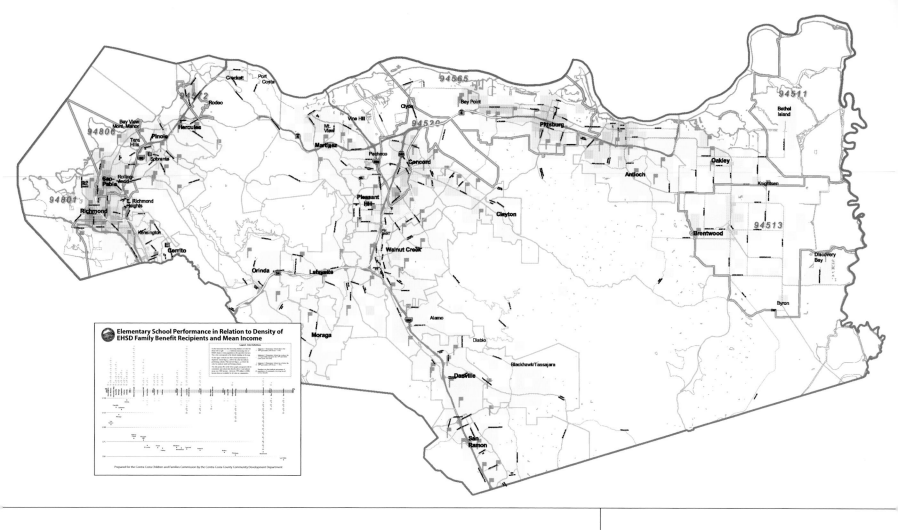

The Contra Costa County Community Development Department produced this map and its associated charts at the request of the Contra Costa Children and Families Commission for use during a planning retreat. At the retreat, the commission used the maps, charts, and other data to determine where services were needed. The two major data categories used were school performance and poverty.

The Commission's role is to foster the optimal development of Contra Costa County's young children (zero to five years) by implementing programs, services, and activities designed to improve the health and well-being of young children; increase children's potential to succeed in school; and assist children's families and caregivers in providing for their physical, mental, and emotional growth.

The map illustrates the geographic relationship between individuals receiving social service benefits (a low income indicator) and school performance. The map also displays ZIP Code areas designated as disadvantaged in a 1999 United Way study. The United Way study examined various issues related to poverty including transportation, availability of services, linguistics, and cultural or linguistic barriers.

The inset chart, "Elementary School Performance in Relation to Density of EHSD Family Benefit Recipients and Mean Income," illustrates, by city or community, the relationship between school performance, income, and percentage of social service benefits recipients.

Another chart, "Elementary School Performance by ZIP Code/Number of EHSD Family Benefit Recipients," was created that shows the number of performing and underperforming schools by ZIP Code. The ZIP Codes designated as disadvantaged in the 1999 United Way study were highlighted.

Elementary School Performance and Social Service Benefit Recipients in Contra Costa County

Contra Costa County Community Development Department

Martinez, California, USA

By John W. Cunningham

Contact
John W. Cunningham, jcunn@cd.co.contra-costa.ca.us

Software
ArcView 3.2, Adobe Illustrator, Microsoft Excel, Seagate Crystal Reports, and Windows NT

Printer
HP DesignJet 3500CP

Data Source(s)
Contra Costa County Employment and Human Services Department, U.S. Census Bureau, Association of Bay Area Governments, Contra Costa County Office of Education, California Department of Education, United Way, Contra Costa Children and Families Commission, and Thomas Bros. Maps

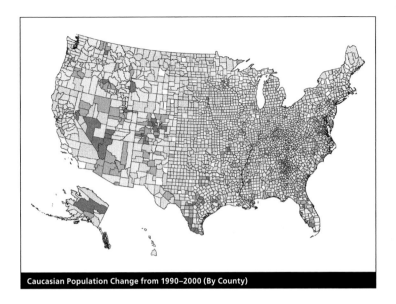

Caucasian Population Change from 1990–2000 (By County)

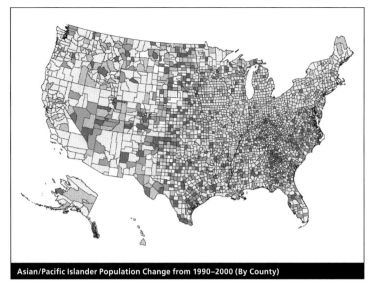

Asian/Pacific Islander Population Change from 1990–2000 (By County)

Percent Change
- > - 50%
- - 1% to - 50%
- No Change
- 1% to 99%
- 100% to 200%
- > 200%

Percent Change
- > - 50%
- - 1% to - 50%
- No Change
- 1% to 99%
- 100% to 200%
- > 200%

Percent Change
- > - 50%
- - 1% to - 50%
- No Change
- 1% to 99%
- 100% to 200%
- > 200%

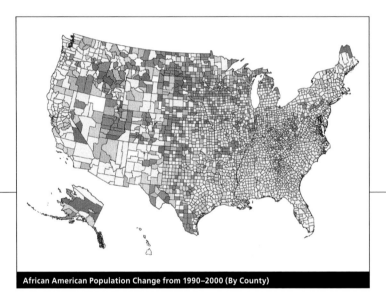

African American Population Change from 1990–2000 (By County)

The Changing Demography of the United States Racial Group with the Greatest Proportionate Increase in Total County Population, 1990–2000

Applied Geographics, Inc.

Boston, Massachusetts, USA

By Joan Gardner and Vicky Tam

Contact
Joan Gardner, jng@appgeo.com

Software
ArcInfo and Windows NT

Printer
HP DesignJet 750C

Data Source(s)
U.S. Census Bureau and others

The changing demography of the United States is presented in a series of thematic maps focusing on changes in the racial breakdown of county-level populations. The maps compare the 1990 and 2000 U.S. census results. The main map indicates which racial groups had the largest increase in their proportion of total county population from 1990 to 2000. Additional maps indicate the range of percentage change in county population for three main racial groups—Caucasian, African American, and Asian.

An additional map indicates the percentage of county population reporting as multiracial or having two or more racial backgrounds in the 2000 census—a new category of data. The overall demographic mapping and analysis project is part of the work of Applied Geographics, Inc. (AGI), which assists the Centers for Medicare and Medicaid Services (CMS—formerly the Health Care Finance Administration) to enhance the targeting of its social marketing and beneficiary services initiatives and mailings. AGI is assisting CMS in developing GIS capacity and disseminating map-based information over the Web.

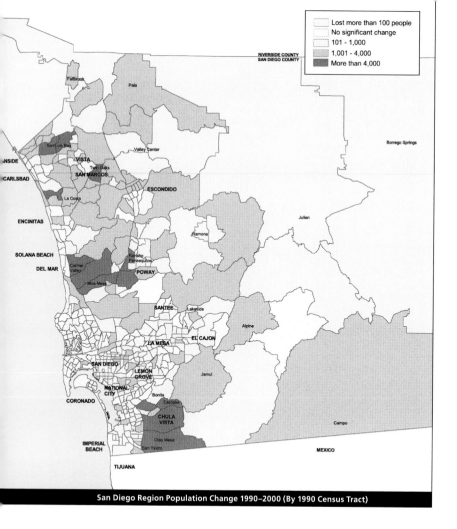

San Diego Region Population Change 1990–2000 (By 1990 Census Tract)

Legend (left map)
Lost more than 100 people
No significant change
101 - 1,000
1,001 - 4,000
More than 4,000

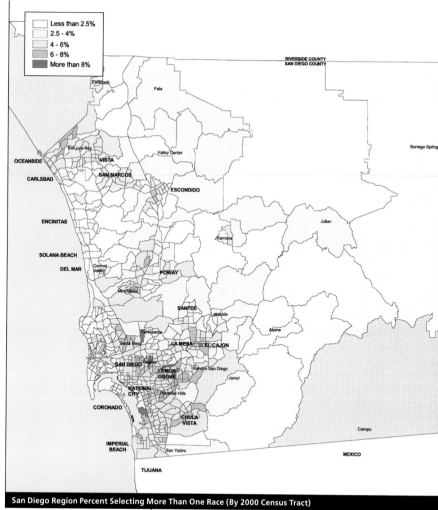

San Diego Region Percent Selecting More Than One Race (By 2000 Census Tract)

Legend (right map)
Less than 2.5%
2.5 - 4%
4 - 6%
6 - 8%
More than 8%

According to Census 2000 reports, the San Diego region's population reached 2,813,833, a 13 percent increase from the 1990 census figure of 2,498,016. This growth rate is nearly identical to the state's and the nation's, marking the first time that California has grown at a pace slower than the nation and the first time since the early 1900s that San Diego's decade growth rate did not exceed California's.

The map on the left shows population change between 1990 and 2000 for San Diego region 1990 census tracts. There are pockets of high growth (more than 4,000 people per census tract) throughout the western part of the region. Other significant growth occurred in inland north county areas and in some east county communities. Several neighborhoods in the older parts of the region and some jurisdictions showed a loss of population or no significant growth.

For the first time in any census, respondents to Census 2000 were allowed to identify themselves as being in more than one race group. In the San Diego region, 4.7 percent (131,976 people) selected more than one race group. This is identical to the statewide percentage, but higher than the national figure of 2.4 percent. Of those selecting more than one race, more than nine out of 10 selected two races, 6 percent selected three races, and 1 percent selected four or more races.

The map on the right displays this information by census tract for the region. The greatest concentration of people selecting more than one race are in the central neighborhood of the City of San Diego and parts of Lemon Grove, El Cajon, Chula Vista, Escondido, and Oceanside.

The First Look at Census 2000

San Diego Association of Governments (SANDAG)

San Diego, California, USA

By Kim Mathis

Contact

Kim Mathis, kma@sandag.org

Software

ArcView and Windows NT

Printer

HP DesignJet 750

Data Source(s)

U.S. Census Bureau and SANDAG

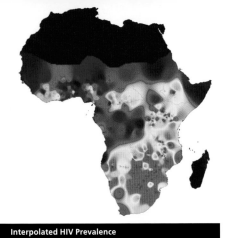

Interpolated HIV Prevalence

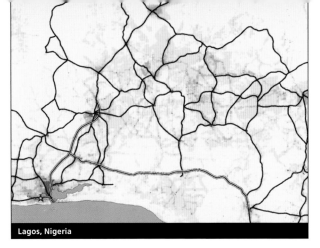

Lagos, Nigeria

Addis Ababa, Ethiopia

Target Population Density (15–49 Year-Olds)

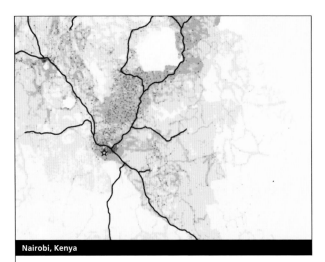

Nairobi, Kenya

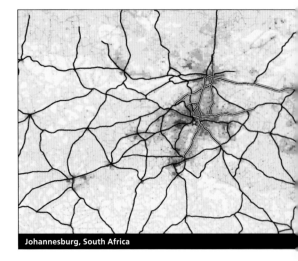

Johannesburg, South Africa

Africa: Applying GIS to the AIDS Pandemic

Central Intelligence Agency, Office of
Transnational Issues

Washington, D.C., USA

By Central Intelligence Agency

Contact
Christopher Price, chrisbp@ucia.gov

Software
ArcInfo 8.1, ArcInfo 7.2.1, ArcView 3.2a, ArcGrid,
and Windows NT

Hardware
Sun and SGI

Printer
Cymbolic Sciences

Data Source(s)
U.S. Census Bureau, Joint United Nations Programme
on HIV/AIDS, ESRI, and Oak Ridge National Laboratory

The U.S. Central Intelligence Agency wanted a product that would enable analysts at the Office of Transnational Issues to better understand the distribution of HIV cases across Africa. Most representations of HIV prevalence in Africa were done based on national infection rates. Such analysis highlights countries that are suffering greatest in proportion to their own populations but does not clearly indicate actual numbers of infected people because population density is not considered.

This map product calculates HIV prevalence for all of Africa using U.S. Census Bureau and Joint United Nations Programme on HIV/AIDS data. It multiplies the interpolated figure by the number of people listed in the LandScan 2000 distributed population database, modified for each country's target population cohort. The result is a grid of one-square-kilometer cells that represents the HIV-positive population while accounting for the dynamics of population density and complex HIV prevalence distribution.

To create the final product showing the number of HIV cases per square kilometer, the cell values of the interpolated HIV prevalence map were divided by 100 and multiplied by the values in the modified population database. The extent was set the same as the buffer, the cell size was set for 0.0833 decimal degrees, and the coverages were multiplied using ArcGrid. The result is a map that shows approximately how many HIV cases exist in each square kilometer on the African continent.

Results indicate that several sub-Saharan countries have significantly infected populations that have gone largely unnoticed in traditional analytical studies. This new method of mapping the disease enables various government offices and nongovernment organizations to reexamine issues, such as resource allocation, regional stability, fiscal aid, and prevention efforts, across the continent.

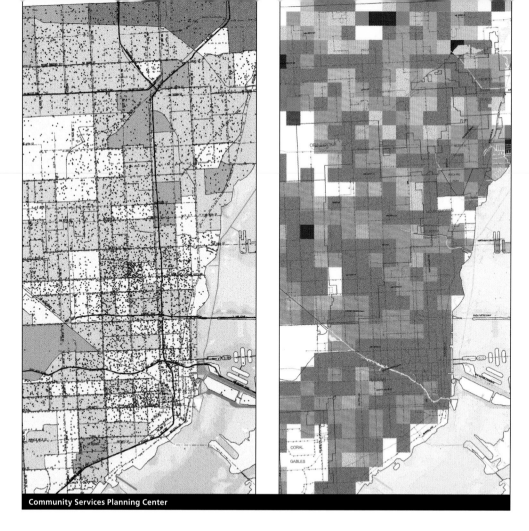

Community Services Planning Center

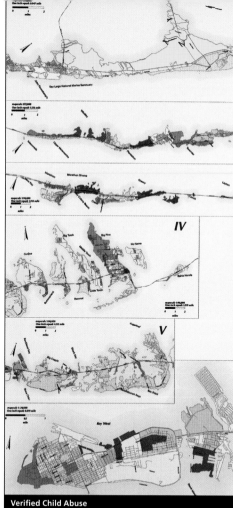

Verified Child Abuse

The Community Services Planning Center (CSPC) created this poster series for the project, Improving Welfare-to-Work Transportation Planning, which required a list of demographic and indicator data including the average distance from each welfare recipient to the closest bus stop. The CSPC receives monthly updates from Florida's computerized Work and Gain Economic Self-Sufficiency (WAGES) system. The objective was to attach the component of the shortest walking distance to the closest public bus stop to each participant record and aggregate the data at the census tract level while computing the average walking distance for each tract. This study displays at the U.S. census block level the average walking distance from a WAGES customer to the closest public bus stop in Miami–Dade County, Florida. The analysis results were used for a detailed study on transportation needs of people in social programs and to apply for a federal grant, which was awarded to the Metropolitan Planning Organization, a local planning agency.

Verified Child Abuse

The Florida Department of Children and Families is charged with providing comprehensive protective services for abused or neglected children in the state by requiring that reports of each abused or neglected child be made to the Florida Abuse Hotline. The Community Services Planning Center collects, geoprocesses, and aggregates child abuse data back to the U.S. census tract level, as presented in this poster. These maps are used for planning and advocacy within the district by the department and by community stakeholders. This map shows year 2000 incidents of verified child abuse in Monroe County (primarily the Florida Keys) with rates calculated per 1,000 children in the population according to the year 2000 U.S. census. These maps also help the department to relocate service centers.

Community Services Maps
State of Florida, Department of Children and Families, Community Services Planning Center

Miami, Florida, USA

By Luis Cespedes, Dwight Danie, Osmel Lopez, and Sifu Zhou

Contact
Osmel Lopez, osmel_lopez@dcf.state.fl.us

Software
ArcInfo 8.0.2, ArcView 3.2, ArcView Spatial Analyst, ArcView Network Analyst, Sun Solaris, and Windows NT

Printer
HP DesignJet 750C

Data Source(s)
State of Florida, Work and Gain Economic Self-Sufficiency System, and Florida Abuse Hotline Information System

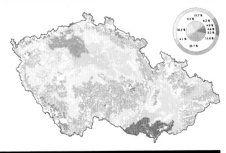

Climatic Zone

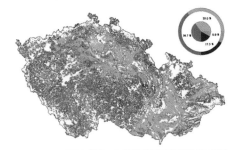

Depth of Soil and Share of Stones

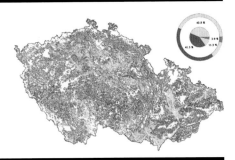

Slope of Agricultural Land

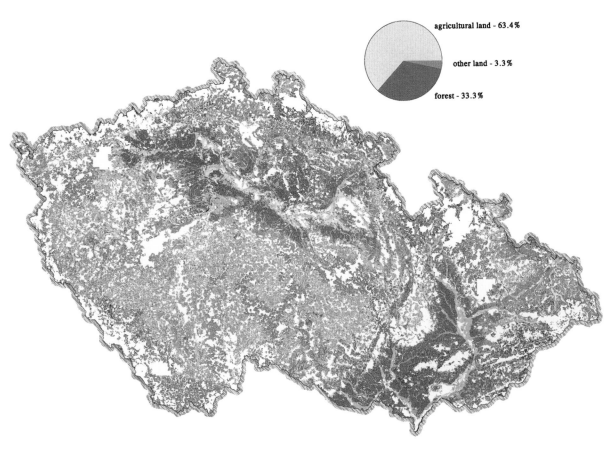

agricultural land - 63.4 %

other land - 3.3 %

forest - 33.3 %

Soil Type Groups

Ecologically Valuated Soil Units—
Digital Cadastral Maps
VUMOP PRAHA

Prague, Czech Republic

By Dagmar Vetiskova and Jan Zohorna

Contact
Dagmar Vetiskova, dasa@vumop.tel.cz

Software
ArcInfo 7.1.2 and UNIX Sun Solaris 5.6

Printer
HP DesignJet 750C

Data Source(s)
Soil Information Database of Research Institute for Soil and Water Conservation

The Research Institute for Soil and Water Conservation is part of the Ministry of Agriculture of the Czech Republic. The institute conducts research and projects in the areas of soil water management and soil science and provides expertise in these fields. At the same time, the institute addresses practical problems of agriculture on a national scale such as preparing the documentation for introduction of a land valuation system into the land register and maintaining the national soil database.

The institute comprises six divisions. A working team for the geographic information systems has been incorporated into the division of Soil Valuation and Mapping. Its tasks involve digitizing and continually updating land valuation maps, maintaining a library of land valuation maps and the related numerical database for the entire Czech Republic, producing maps for local authorities, processing and evaluating data extracted from the numerical database of land valuation, developing and improving methods for digitizing the land valuation maps including consulting with local agencies, and participating in research projects requiring applications of GIS.

The Soil Information Database was generated from terrain maps in 1:5,000 scale and includes the area of the Czech Republic. All of the agricultural land (plowed land, grassland, and special land such as hops gardens and vineyards) has been mapped.

The Soil Information Database contains ecologically valuated soil units. Soil units include five numbers (agricultural land) or two numbers (nonagricultural land). The database is being transferred to cadastral maps in 1:2,880 and 1:2,000 scale and will be adjusted according to compatibility with the information system of the real estate land register.

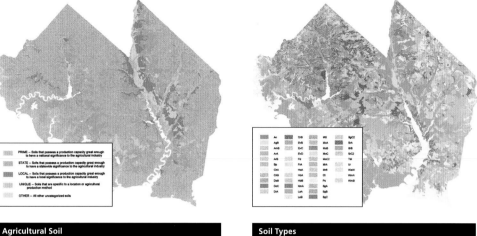

Agricultural Soil

Legend:
- PRIME — Soils that possess a production capacity great enough to have a national significance to the agricultural industry
- STATE — Soils that possess a production capacity great enough to have a statewide significance to the agricultural industry
- LOCAL — Soils that possess a production capacity great enough to have a local significance to the agricultural industry
- UNIQUE — Soils that are specific to a location or agricultural production method
- OTHER — All other uncategorized soils

Soil Types

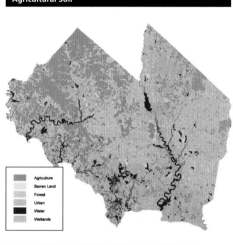

Wetlands

Legend:
- Agriculture
- Barren Land
- Forest
- Urban
- Water
- Wetlands

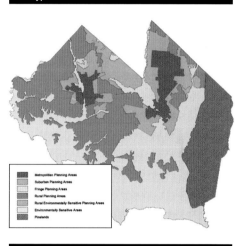

State Planning Areas

Legend:
- Metropolitan Planning Areas
- Suburban Planning Areas
- Fringe Planning Areas
- Rural Planning Areas
- Rural Environmentally Sensitive Planning Areas
- Environmentally Sensitive Areas
- Pinelands

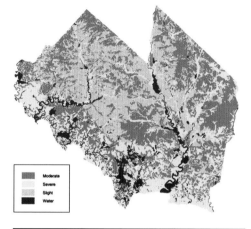

Septic Suitablility (Percolation Rate)

Legend:
- Moderate
- Severe
- Slight
- Water

The New Jersey State Agriculture Development Committee (SADC) administers and coordinates the state's farmland preservation programs. These programs protect farmland by placing deed restrictions that prohibit nonagricultural development. Landowners who permanently deed-restrict their farms against future nonagricultural development are monetarily compensated for the development value of the farmland.

New Jersey faces an extreme degree of development pressure because it possesses the highest population density of any state in the nation. Known as the Garden State, New Jersey is actively and vociferously implementing a variety of programs and legislation that will preserve the bucolic agrarian landscape that still exists in a large portion of the state. Most of the pristine agricultural environment within the state exists within its southernmost counties, of which Cumberland County is among the largest and least developed. Consequently, the Farmland Preservation Program within Cumberland County is one of the most comprehensive in the state.

The application process for the Farmland Preservation Program is very competitive. Farms are scored based on several factors including the size of the farm, soil typology, surrounding land use, and other considerations that could affect the significance of the farm as an agricultural producer.

Within the category of soil productivity, there are several separate considerations. The maps on this page show septic suitability or percolation rate of the soil, agricultural soil classifications, and soil types within Cumberland County. Other considerations are wetlands locations and state planning areas. All of these considerations were presented with a narrative explanation on an educational poster, which is available in digital format from the Cumberland County Department of Planning and Development.

Cumberland County Farmland Preservation Program—Criteria for Evaluation
Cumberland County Department of Planning and Development

Bridgeton, New Jersey, USA

By Kimberly Brown, Sharon Mollick, and Matthew E. Pisarski

Contact
Matthew E. Pisarski, mattpi@co.cumberland.nj.us

Software
ArcView 3.2 and Windows NT

Printer
HP DesignJet 755CM

Data Source(s)
New Jersey (NJ) Department of Environmental Protection, Cumberland County Planning and Development, NJ State Agriculture Development Committee, NJ Office of State Planning, and NJ Farm Bureau

Cumberland County Department of Planning and Development

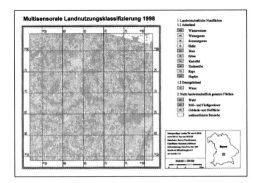

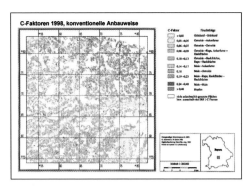

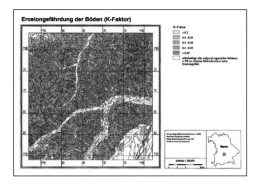

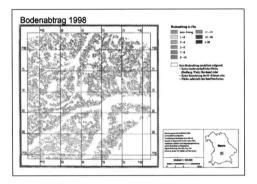

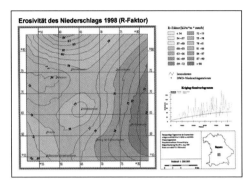

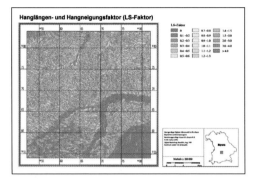

Remote Sensing and GIS in Soil Erosion Modeling

Hessian National Institute for Environment and Geology (HLUG)

Wiesbaden, Germany

By Petra Fritz

Contact
Petra Fritz, p.fritz@hlug.de

Software
ArcInfo 7.2.1, ArcGrid, ArcTIN™, ERDAS IMAGINE 8.3, and SPSS

Hardware
SGI

Printer
HP DesignJet 2000CP

Data Source(s)
Landsat TM, SPOT, IRS-1C, topographic maps, land use ground-truth data captured on a field GIS, digital field map of agricultural land, digital elevation models, Bavarian Land Survey Office, German Meteorological Service, and Bavarian Geological Survey

The prevention of soil loss by water erosion and the protection of natural resources particularly with regard to soils are aspects of sustainable land use systems. A primary prerequisite for reasonable soil protection is a realistic estimation of the effective soil erosion of agriculturally used areas. A quantitative estimation of soil erosion on a medium map scale for larger regions was done with the well-established and still up-to-date Universal Soil Loss Equation (USLE) and applied with a modified calculation of the LS-factor (terrain factor). The relevant geofactors to calculate the soil erosion using the USLE are the R-factor (erosion factor), the K-factor (soil factor), the LS-factor, and the C-factor (land use factor). All data layers are integrated as raster data (ArcInfo GRIDs) into the model to minimize error propagation through the multiplicative combination of the data.

The two main objectives presented on the poster are the retrieval of the C-factor using remotely sensed optical satellite data and the modified calculation of the LS-factor. Using multitemporal classification of remote sensing data, satellite data was analyzed over three consecutive years. The overall accuracies of the year-to-year crop classification results varied between 82 and 87 percent using the maximum likelihood classifier. The C-factor, which is based on crop rotation systems over two to three years, was determined by the land use classification results of three consecutive years.

Another objective of this study involved a three-dimensional analysis of the terrain surface for an optimized calculation of the LS-factor. Additional studies addressed the influence of an improved high-resolution digital elevation model (DEM) with a 5-meter cell size on the calculation results of the LS-factor and the final soil loss. It could be demonstrated that the mean LS-factor and the mean soil loss are almost three times higher when the 5-meter DEM is used. These results showed clearly that the LS-factor and the total soil loss is strongly influenced by the quality of the DEM database.

Vegetation Communities—McArthur Study Area, Yukon Territory

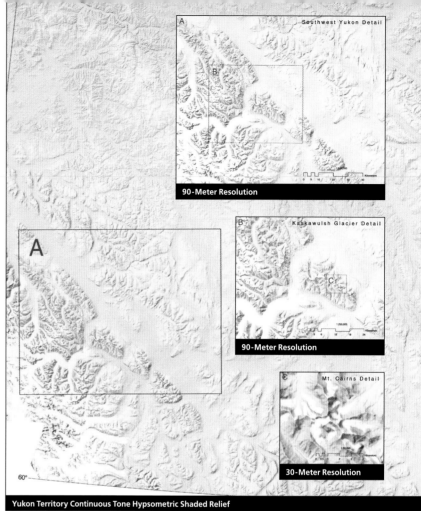

A

B   Southwest Yukon Detail
90-Meter Resolution

B   Kaskawulsh Glacier Detail
90-Meter Resolution

C   Mt. Cairns Detail
30-Meter Resolution

60°

Yukon Territory Continuous Tone Hypsometric Shaded Relief

Vegetation Communities—McArthur Study Area, Yukon Territory

This map was produced to facilitate ground-truthing of photogrammetrically derived vegetation communities by vegetation specialists working in remote central Yukon. Although maps have always been a part of department fieldwork, this map's addition of shaded relief sets it apart. This simple improvement enables users to draw inferences between vegetation communities and physiography more readily than from a contour map. To achieve the colored relief, GRID functions were used to integrate colored vegetation polygons with a hillshade grid. The net result was an RGB grid composite, which was converted to a GeoTIFF for use with ArcInfo. Although more involved than manipulating a transparency slider bar, the result is visually striking. An additional and unforeseen benefit of shaded relief was that it enhanced the ability of helicopter-borne field crews to locate specific vegetation units from the air. The final copies were printed on HP Tyvek, making the field maps able to withstand the rigors of fieldwork in the harsh mountain environment.

Yukon Territory Continuous Tone Hypsometric Shaded Relief

This map highlights the 30-meter digital elevation models (DEMs) created by the Yukon Department of Environment. The entire Yukon data set consists of more than 800 7.5-minute DEMs, which fully integrate with the DEMs of adjacent Alaska, British Columbia, and Northwest Territories. They were resampled to 90 meters as a mosaic to create the continuous tone shaded relief used in this map. This product is a first step toward producing a 1:1,000,000-scale topographic relief map of the Yukon Territory. The colored relief was generated using a GRID methodology similar to that applied to the Vegetation Communities map. The continuous tone effect was achieved by mathematically ramping RGB values between selected color breaks (green to gray to yellow to red) to produce a color table that could simulate a smooth transition across all colors—a total of 308 color values in this instance. The finishing touch involved integrating glacial ice fields into the image.

Yukon Territory Maps
Yukon Department of Environment
Whitehorse, Yukon, Canada
By Gerry Perrier

Contact
Gerry Perrier, gerry.perrier@gov.yk.ca

Software
ArcInfo 8.1

Hardware
Dell Precision 620 workstation

Printer
HP DesignJet 1055CM

Data Source(s)
Yukon Department of Environment and Natural Resources, Canada

Forest Cover

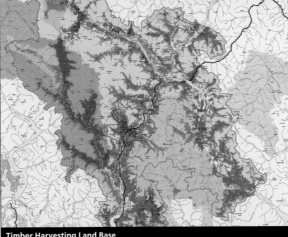

Timber Harvesting Land Base

Biogeoclimatic Ecosystem Classification

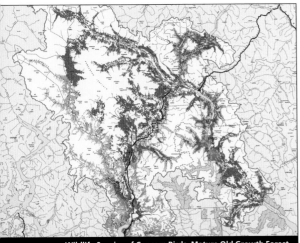

Wildlife Species of Concern Birds, Mature Old Growth Forest

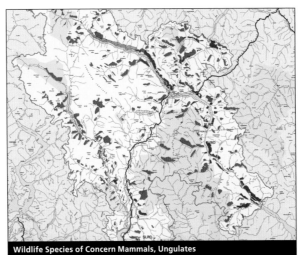

Wildlife Species of Concern Mammals, Ungulates

Visual Resource Management

Sea-to-Sky Land and Resource Management Planning

Ministry of Sustainable Resource Management, Vancouver Region

Surrey, British Columbia, Canada

By Gurdeep Singh

Contact
Gurdeep Singh, gurdeep.singh@gems2.gov.bc.ca

Software
ArcInfo and UNIX

Hardware
HP

Printer
HP DesignJet 1055CM

Data Source(s)
Regional and corporate data warehouses

The Resource Atlas was created as an information and reference tool for the Sea-to-Sky Land and Resource Management Planning Process in the Squamish Forest District. The planning process objective is to produce an integrated land and resource management plan that addresses a range of land and resource uses and interests.

The maps depict the status of land and resources in the Squamish Forest District and are used as a planning tool and for information dissemination to the public. They are useful tools for roundtable discussions in which planners need to address specific issues in certain geographic areas. Wildlife biologists, forest ecosystem specialists, and forest planners also use the maps for operational planning.

Creation of the Resource Atlas involved integrating and analyzing GIS data sets from multiple provincial agencies. Putting all of the relevant land and resource information about Squamish Forest District in one location makes the jobs of planners and other specialists much easier. What previously took days to accomplish—gathering data in different formats, scales, and projections from different agencies and sources—can now be accomplished from a single source.

In addition to the selected maps displayed here, the Resource Atlas provides information on tourism use, commercial and public recreation zones, bedrock geology, water resources, First Nations traditional territories, landscape units, ecosections, park management zones, mineral and placer tenures, roads, fish potential for lakes and streams, and additional wildlife data on species of concern. Additional information about the Resource Atlas is available at srmrpdwww.env.gov.bc.ca/lrmp/s2s/index.htm.

Minist

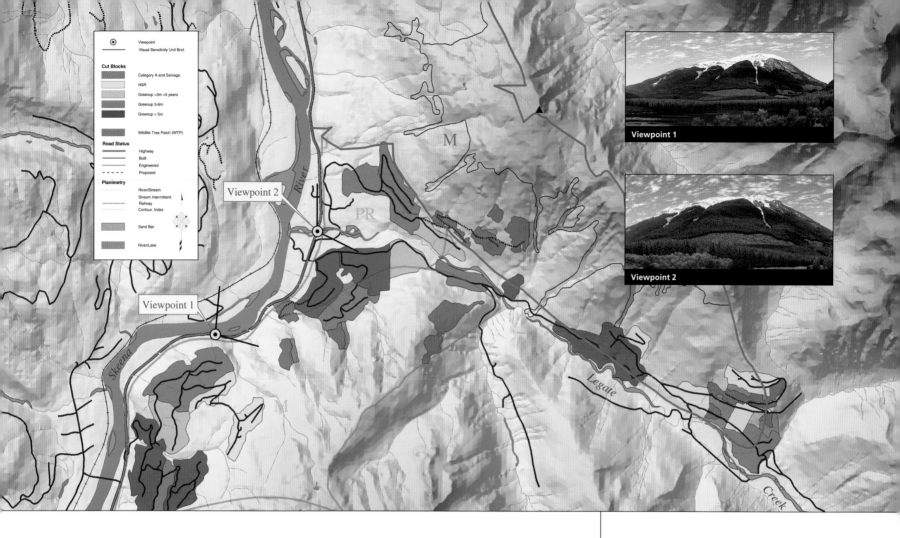

This type of product is typically used as a planning aid or as part of a visual impact assessment government submission. The map was generated primarily using ArcInfo. It incorporates a number of informative images as related to a visual impact assessment.

Two different design aids were used to show the impact of a proposed harvest pattern on the visual landscape. The first is the base map, which identifies proposed block locations and basic planimetric information. Hillshading has been incorporated to provide an additional visual aid to the topography. Hillshading was generated using ArcInfo software's TIN/lattice with a default color gradient pick list.

The second design aid is the use of viewpoint images generated with World Construction Set software using data preprocessed in ArcInfo. The resultant World Construction Set bit maps were placed into the map design to simulate a photorealistic view of the proposed blocks. ArcView was used to capture the boundary of the visible blocks to calculate the percent alteration in perspective view.

A simulation such as this is used to assess whether or not target visual quality objectives have been achieved.

Visual Impact Assessment
Timberline Forest Inventory Consultants

Vancouver, British Columbia, Canada

By Glenn Loveng and Marcel Morin

Contact
Jocelyn Hewson, jrh@timberline.ca

Software
ArcInfo, ArcView, World Construction Set, UNIX, and Windows NT

Hardware
Sun workstation

Printer
HP DesignJet 755CM

Data Source(s)
Client source maps, TRIM 1:20,000 digital base data, and ESRI

Timberline
Forest Inventory Consultants

Geologic Map of Colorado National Monument and Adjacent Areas, Mesa County, Colorado

U.S. Geological Survey (USGS)–Denver Federal Center

Denver, Colorado, USA

By Craig Brunstein, Rex D. Cole, Robert P. Dickerson, Alex Donatich, Anne E. Harding, William C. Hood, James B. Johnson, Richard F. Livaccari, Robert B. Scott, Ralph R. Shroba, Nancy Shock, Carol Quesenberry, and Paco Van Sistine

Contact
Paco Van Sistine, dsistine@usgs.gov

Software
ArcInfo 7.1.2 and Adobe Illustrator

Hardware
Sun and Macintosh

Printer
HP DesignJet 3500

Data Source(s)
Colorado National Monument, U.S. Department of the Interior National Park Service, and USGS

The purpose of this map is to provide a geologic map for the public to use at Colorado National Monument and to provide sufficient geologic information for land use and land management decisions by U.S. National Park Service staff. This new 1:24,000-scale geologic mapping in the Colorado National I-70 Corridor Cooperative Geologic Mapping Project provides new interpretations and data for the stratigraphy, structure, and geologic hazards in the area from the Colorado River in Grand Valley onto the Uncompahgre Plateau.

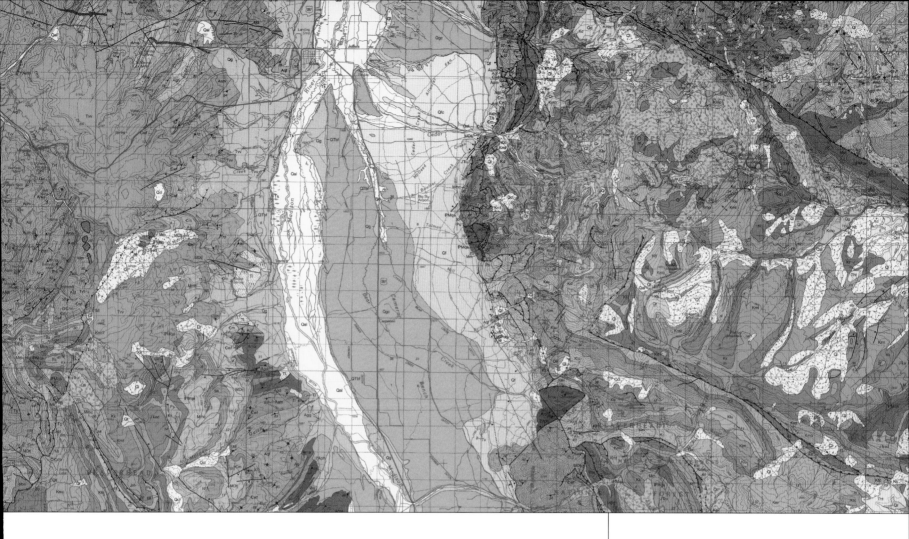

The geology of the Ennis 30-minute by 60-minute quadrangle was compiled at the scale of 1:100,000 from published and unpublished sources (dating from 1961 to 1996) as hand-drafted line work on a scale-stable Mylar base map. The line work was scanned and vectorized with the CADCORE program. Additional lines and points were added by using a digitizer tablet with a resolution of 0.001 inch. Two coverages were initially created, one containing polygons and the other containing all other features such as labels, fold axes, and line decorations. The final database consists of four coverages—one polygon, two line, and one line/point.

This map of the geology of the Ennis 30-minute by 60-minute quadrangle is part of a new geologic map of the state of Montana and was compiled in cooperation with the Montana Bureau of Mines and Geology and the Department of Earth Sciences, Montana State University. The map was designed for a scientific audience and shows the surface distribution of 89 geologic map units and structural features. The layout includes a list of map units, a diagram showing the ages of the map units, and supplemental illustrations that show major structural elements in the quadrangle and sources of information. A pamphlet that contains a discussion of the geology and complete descriptions of the map units is distributed with the printed map.

Geologic Map of the Ennis Quadrangle
U.S. Geological Survey (USGS)

Denver, Colorado, USA

By Karl S. Kellogg and Van S. Williams

Contact
Karl Kellogg, kkellogg@usgs.gov

Software
ArcInfo 7.1.2, Adobe Illustrator 8.0.1, CADCORE, DESIGN-CAD, MAPublisher, and Windows NT

Printer
HP DesignJet 3500

Data Source(s)
USGS

U.S. Geological Survey

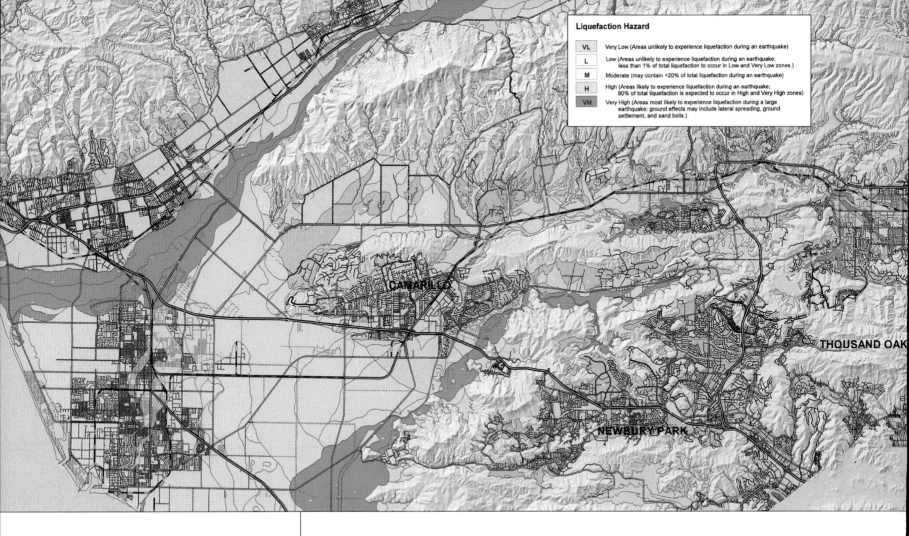

Liquefaction Hazard

VL	Very Low (Areas unlikely to experience liquefaction during an earthquake)
L	Low (Areas unlikely to experience liquefaction during an earthquake; less than 1% of total liquefaction to occur in Low and Very Low zones.)
M	Moderate (may contain <20% of total liquefaction during an earthquake)
H	High (Areas likely to experience liquefaction during an earthquake; 80% of total liquefaction is expected to occur in High and Very High zones)
VH	Very High (Areas most likely to experience liquefaction during a large earthquake; ground effects may include lateral spreading, ground settlement, and sand boils.)

Liquefaction Susceptibility Mapping, Ventura County, California

William Lettis & Associates, Inc., and Ventura County

Ventura, California, USA

By John Helms, Christopher Hitchcock, William Lettis, Scott Lindvall, Carolyn Randolph, and Kristin Weaver, William Lettis & Associates, Inc.; Lynne Kada and Paul Van Zuyle, Ventura County

Contact
Christopher Hitchcock, hitch@lettis.com

Software
ArcView 3.2

Hardware
Apple PowerBook G4

Printer
HP DesignJet 2500CP

Data Source(s)
U.S. Geological Survey, Ventura County, and others

Digital quaternary geologic maps and liquefaction susceptibility maps were constructed at scales of 1:12,000 to 1:24,000 for 23 7.5-minute quadrangles with alluviated areas within Ventura County. These detailed maps, funded by Ventura County and the U.S. Geological Survey National Earthquake Hazard Reduction Program, provide a valuable resource for mitigating potential risks to critical lifelines, petroleum pipelines, and other facilities supporting the large population and active oil industry in the Oxnard–Ventura area and for planning future development in Ventura County.

The maps are being incorporated into Ventura County's countywide GIS. Geological, geotechnical, and hydrological data sets are compiled in a digital database compatible with the California Geological Survey (CGS) ongoing Seismic Hazards Mapping Program. In addition, digital geologic mapping produced for this study provides baseline data from which, in part, the CGS Seismic Hazards Mapping Program currently is developing official liquefaction zone maps.

Liquefaction-related ground settlement and displacement associated with the Northridge earthquake on January 17, 1994, caused considerable damage to private and public property in nearby Simi Valley, California. This damage primarily occurred in saturated Holocene stream deposits and overlying artificial fill at the eastern end of the valley. Much of Simi Valley and the Santa Clara River Valley, the Oxnard Plain, floodplains along the Ventura River, and portions of other populated valleys in Ventura County are underlain by similar historic and Holocene sediments that are susceptible to liquefaction during future large earthquakes.

William Lettis & Associates, Inc., and Ventura County

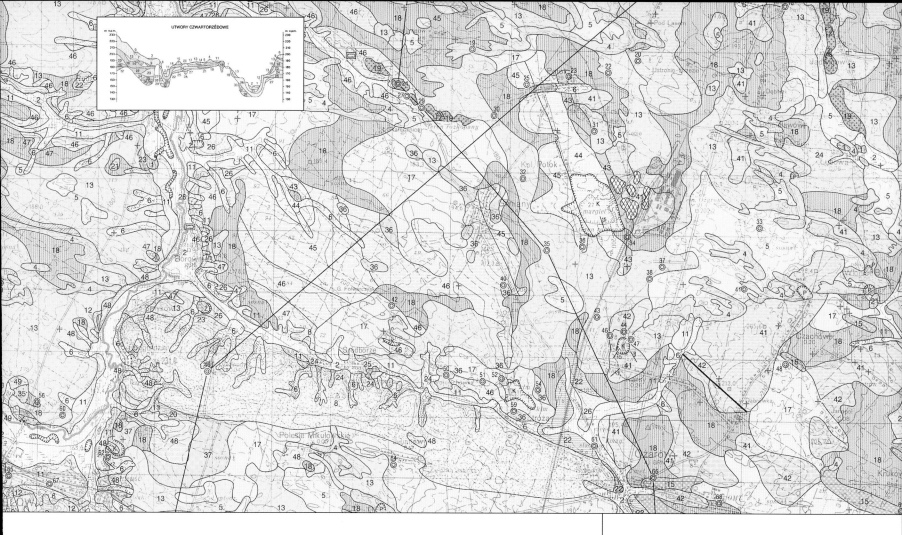

The Detailed Geological map of Poland, at a scale of 1:50,000, is a basic geological map that consists of 1,069 sheets and has been produced since 1952. The Polish Geological Institute has been producing the maps with computer-aided geological mapping since 1994. The mapping process consists of database creation, computer-aided technical editing, and preparation for printing the map sheets.

Two applications were developed to assist with the tasks—ArcSMGP and KODA. These ARC Macro Language applications use ArcInfo and Oracle capabilities for procedural automation. ArcSMGP and KODA are designed for geological database creators and technical map editors. These applications have been improved and developed every year in collaboration with Neokart GIS.

Sheet Ozarow (819) was printed by the offset method in 1998. The offset films were produced at 2,540 dpi resolution. Map sheets had been printed with the offset method until 1999. Since 2000, sheets have been plotted on demand, and only the three most important sheets will be printed every third year by the offset method. PostScript files of map sheets are converted to raster format by ArcPress. The Polish Geological Institute is replacing IRIX with Windows NT environment for the map production.

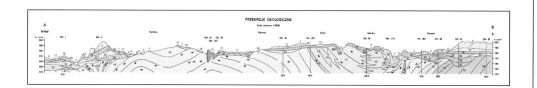

The Detailed Geological Map of Poland, Sheet Ozarow (819)
Polish Geological Institute

Warsaw, Poland

By T. Bielecki, I. Kalinowska, A. Myscichowski, and Z. Zlonkiewicz

Contact
Waldemar Gogolek, wgog@pgi.waw.pl

Software
ArcInfo, ArcPress, Oracle, ArcSMGP, and KODA (ARC Macro Language applications for database production and technical editing), IRIX, and Windows NT

Hardware
SGI workstations

Printer
Offset printer and HP DesignJet 2500CP

Data Source(s)
Polish Geological Institute and database of the Detailed Geological Map of Poland

Polish Geological Institute

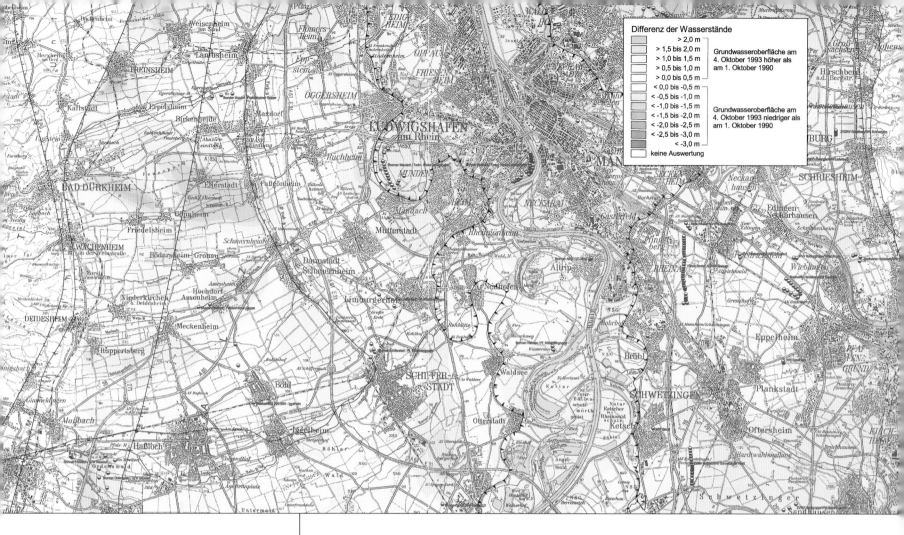

Differenz der Wasserstände

	> 2,0 m
	> 1,5 bis 2,0 m
	> 1,0 bis 1,5 m
	> 0,5 bis 1,0 m
	> 0,0 bis 0,5 m

Grundwasseroberfläche am
4. Oktober 1993 höher als
am 1. Oktober 1990

	< 0,0 bis -0,5 m
	< -0,5 bis -1,0 m
	< -1,0 bis -1,5 m
	< -1,5 bis -2,0 m
	< -2,0 bis -2,5 m
	< -2,5 bis -3,0 m
	< -3,0 m

Grundwasseroberfläche am
4. Oktober 1993 niedriger als
am 1. Oktober 1990

keine Auswertung

The Difference in Groundwater Between October 1990 and October 1993

GDV Gesellschaft für Geografische Datenverarbeitung GmbH

Ingelheim, Germany

By Joachim Mueller

Contact
Thomas Riehl, riehl@gdv.com

Software
ArcView 3.2

Printer
HP DesignJet 2500CP

Data Source(s)
Geodata sets from various state agencies

Hydrogeological Mapping and Groundwater Management in the Rhine–Neckar Area

The Rhine–Neckar area is one of the most important economic and urban centers of southwest Germany. A large population increase in conjunction with growing industries led to a severe use of groundwater resources from the mid-20th century on. Because of this, a comprehensive examination of groundwater quality and management became necessary.

In the course of long-term studies, geological, hydrological, and groundwater data was collected and a groundwater model developed. As a part of the final report, a collection of 18 maps visualizing the GIS data of different origins was produced.

These maps show the thickness and spreading of the groundwater horizons, the height of the groundwater level, and the chemical and physical condition of the groundwater as well as different prediction schemes of the groundwater model.

The results of the study are the basis for answering questions about groundwater protection and future groundwater management in the Rhine–Neckar area.

This map shows the difference in the level of upper groundwater in the Rhine–Neckar area between October 1, 1990, and October 4, 1993. The yellow or green colored areas represent a rise in the upper groundwater level during the examination. The red color marks areas where the groundwater level dropped.

GDV Gesellschaft für Geografische Datenverarbeitung GmbH

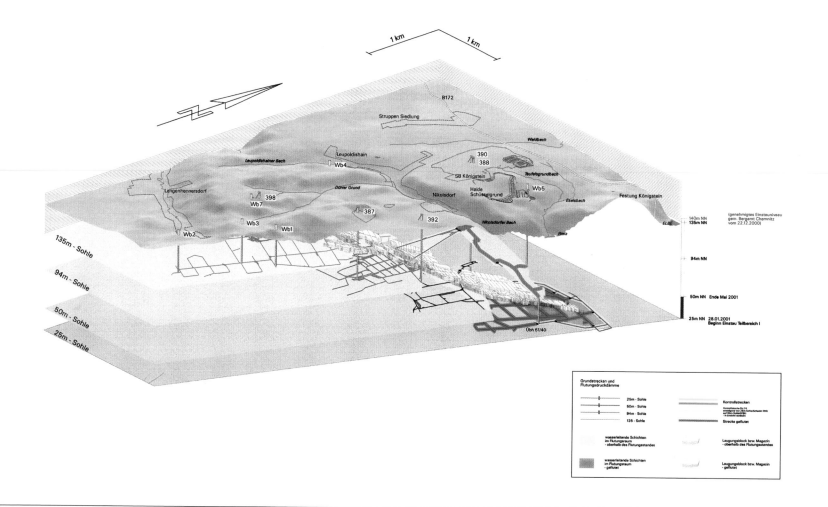

The unique geological situation at the Königstein deposit (uranium mineralization in a sandstone aquifer) allowed mining by what became known as "in situ block leaching." Blocks of uranium-bearing rock were blasted underground to increase permeability and surface areas before being leached with sulphuric acid.

Approximately 1.9 million cubic meters of acidic solution are contained as pore fluid in the rock. These maps display a three-dimensional description of the underground mine workings and leaching blocks—the geological profile, the concept of flooding, and the effect of the control drift. The complete map composition was created in ArcInfo.

Flooding of Underground Uranium Mine Workings

WISMUT GmbH

Chemnitz, Germany

By Hermann Rasch

Contact
Hermann Rasch, h.rasch@wismut.de

Software
ArcInfo 8.0.2, ArcGrid, and ArcTIN

Hardware
HP

Printer
HP DesignJet 650C

Data Source(s)
WISMUT GmbH

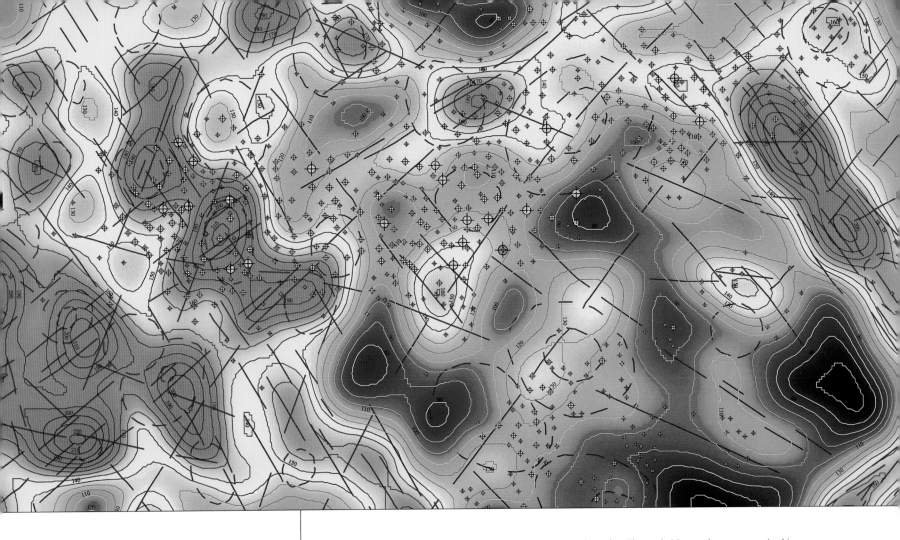

Fracture Density and Direction with Well Location Correlation Analysis

Earth Satellite Corporation (EarthSat)

Rockville, Maryland, USA

By Mike Blank and Jeffrey Miller

Contact
Christopher Schierkolk, cschierkolk@earthsat.com

Software
ArcInfo, ArcGrid, and Windows 2000

Printer
HP DesignJet 3500CP

Data Source(s)
Landsat Thematic Mapper Imagery 2000

Earth Satellite Corporation (EarthSat) geologists interpreted Landsat Thematic Mapper imagery acquired in 2000 for surface fractures. The fracture information (location, orientation, and direction) was stored in an ArcInfo spatial database, and EarthSat used ArcGrid to model surfaces that characterize the regional density and direction of these fractures.

Like traditional rose diagrams, these surfaces assist petroleum geologists in site selection and characterization for drilling. EarthSat used the surface results to quantify the relationship between well productivity and coincident regional fracture orientation and density.

These methods are used to identify possible drilling sites for oil and gas extraction. The density and direction of the interpreted fractures help correlate and deduce which areas are best suited for drilling. The fracture density surface is created using a 100-meter cell resolution and a 2.4-kilometer sampling radius for each cell. Correlations can be made with fracture density highs and well locations.

The average direction surface is created using a 100-meter cell resolution and a five-kilometer sampling radius for each cell. Correlations can be made with average fracture direction areas and well locations.

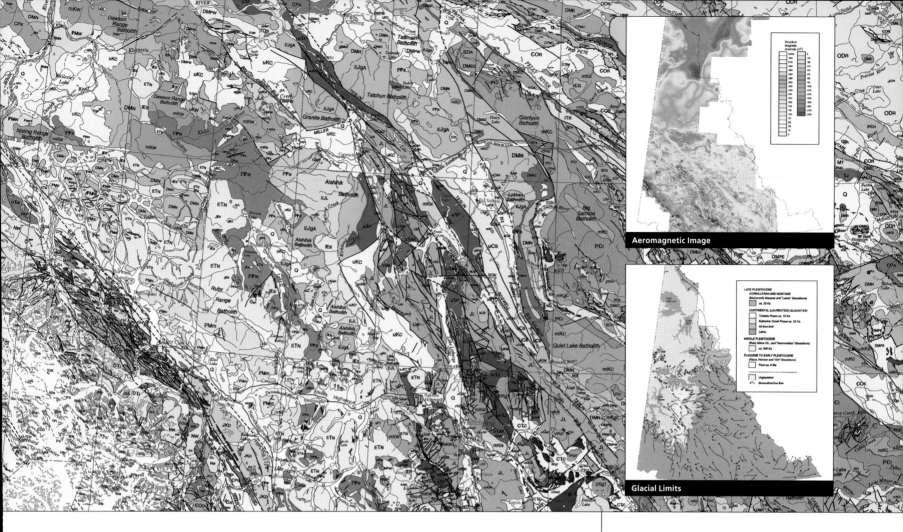

Aeromagnetic Image

Glacial Limits

Bedrock Geology, Yukon Territory, was compiled from 128 different data sources, mostly paper maps ranging from 1:50,000 scale to 1:250,000 scale that were published by the Yukon Geology Program and the Geological Survey of Canada. The compilation is available both as a digital product on CD–ROM (complete with viewer) and as a 1:1,000,000-scale hard-copy map (Geological Survey of Canada Open File D3826 and 3754, respectively).

Digitizing and compiling the large number of source maps was time-consuming and involved many stages of iterative visual and automated error checking. The source maps were compiled to produce a single map for each Canadian National Topographical System (NTS) 1:250,000-scale map area. The completed maps for each NTS map area were compiled into a single Yukon-wide coverage with corrected boundary mismatches. An automated error checking routine was developed using ARC Macro Language to identify inconsistencies between arcs and adjacent polygons. During and at the end of this stage, a regional legend was synthesized from the compilation of original map legends.

The result is a new seamless bedrock geological map for the Yukon Territory comprising some 33,100 polygons and 87,600 arcs. The data on the CD is formatted as an ArcInfo library, Arc Interchange (.e00), and shapefiles at a nominal scale of 1:250,000 or better. The CD version also comes with several other data sets compiled by different authors including geochronology, paleontology, surficial features, parks, mineral occurrences, physiography, topography, and aeromagnetics. The bedrock digital data was generalized to a scale of 1:1,000,000, and other cartographic improvements were made in ArcInfo to produce the bedrock geology hard-copy map.

Bedrock Geology, Yukon Territory
Geological Survey of Canada,
Natural Resources Canada

Vancouver, British Columbia, Canada

By S.P. Gordey, A.J. Makepeace, and C.L. Wagner

Contact
Steve Gordey, sgordey@gsc.nrcan.gc.ca

Software
ArcInfo 7, Digital UNIX, and Windows NT

Hardware
DEC 3000 Alpha and Pentium III

Printer
HP DesignJet 5000

Data Source(s)
Various

Geological Survey of Canada, Natural Resources Canada

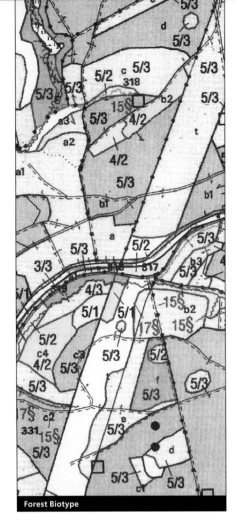
Forest Biotype

Forest Site

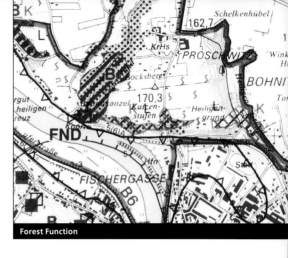
Forest Function

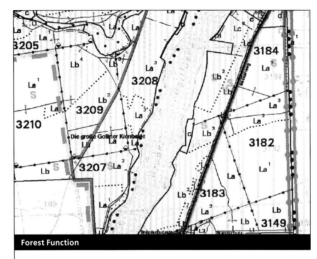
Forest Function

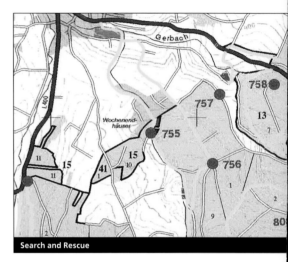
Search and Rescue

GIS in Forest Administration of the Federation and the States of the Federal Republic of Germany

HGN Hydrogeologie GmbH, Torgau Branch

Torgau, Germany

By Jens Forberig

Contact
Dieter Hagen, d.hagen@hgn-online.de

Software
ArcInfo 8.0.2, Microsoft PowerPoint, and Windows NT

Hardware
Sun Ultra 1 workstations

Printer
HP DesignJet 1055CM

Data Source(s)
Forest Administration of the Federal Republic of Germany, Forest Administration of Brandenburg, Forest Administration of Rhineland–Palatinate, Forest Administration of Saxonia, and Forest Administration of Saxonia–Anhalt

In the last few years, the forest administrations of the Federation and States of the Federal Republic of Germany have implemented computer-based methods for forest resource mapping. Databases are available for the entire range of forest-related tasks.

Specific data is linked with spatial data for forest management—Forestry GIS. The digital forest base map or forest district map serves as the base map for all other thematic forestry maps that are derived from the Forestry GIS.

Forestry GIS receives data from working maps and original field books, which are created when directly documenting information in the forest, and from specialized forestry databases. The key to faster and more efficient forestry departments lies in the processing of the forestry data in one common system and in deriving thematic forestry maps from the Forestry GIS. Preparing Forestry GIS requires intensive development of services and involves programming GIS components, recording and updating a range of forestry information, and converting data from various forest administrations' databases that differ substantially in format from Forestry GIS.

The map shows a cross section of thematic forestry maps from several forest administrations at the federal and state levels, which have been prepared based on specific GIS solutions by the Torgau Branch of HGN Hydrogeologie GmbH.

The map and legend extracts come from a forest site map, a forest planning map, a forestry operation or forest stand map, a forest function map, an aerial map, a search and rescue map, and a forest biotope map.

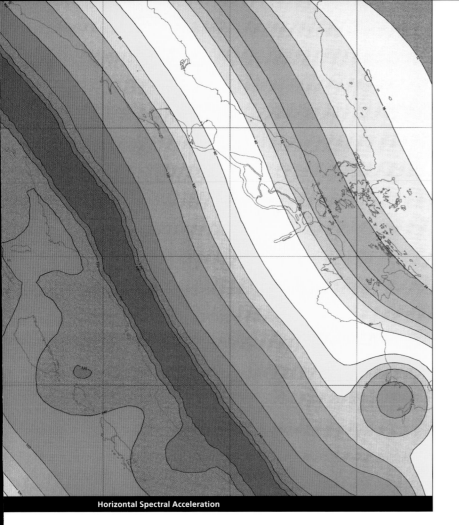

Horizontal Spectral Acceleration

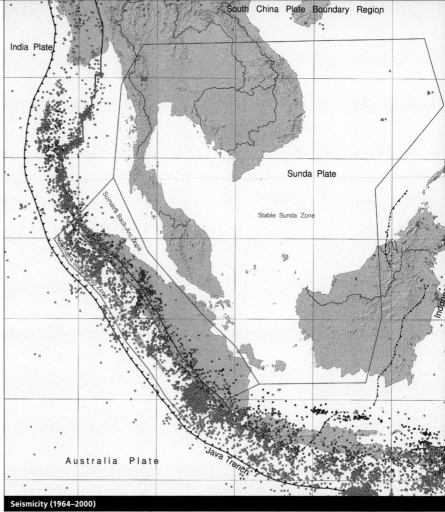

South China Plate Boundary Region

India Plate

Sunda Plate

Stable Sunda Zone

Sumatra Back-Arc Zone

Australia Plate

Java Trench

Seismicity (1964–2000)

Seismic hazard maps produced by the U.S. Geological Survey are based on current information about the rate at which earthquakes occur in different areas and how far earthquake shaking extends from the earthquake source.

By estimating the shaking hazard from earthquakes, scientists and engineers are laying the groundwork for providing information about designing infrastructure that can resist the effects of earthquakes. Buildings, bridges, highways, and utilities built to meet the estimated shaking hazard not only save lives but also enable critical activities to continue with less disruption. This is important in a world where natural disasters such as earthquakes can have far-reaching effects outside the disaster's impact area.

The Horizontal Spectral Acceleration map shows acceleration for a 0.2 second period (5 percent of critical damping) with 2 percent probability of exceedance in 50 years.

The map on the right displays 1964–2000 seismicity in southeast Asia and seismic source zones used in hazard analysis.

Seismic Hazard Maps for Southeast Asia
U.S. Geological Survey (USGS)

Denver, Colorado, USA

By Mark Petersen and Ken Rukstales

Contact
Ken Rukstales, rukstales@usgs.gov

Software
ArcInfo 8.0.1 and Windows NT

Printer
HP DesignJet 2500

Data Source(s)
USGS

U.S. Geological Survey

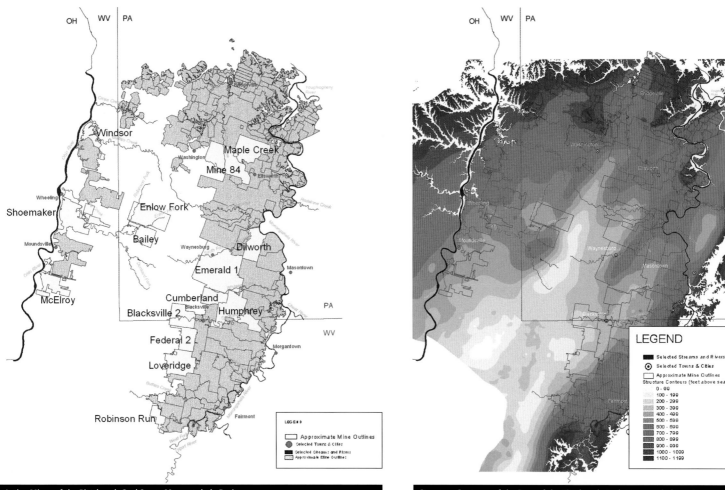

Active Mines of the Pittsburgh Coal Seam, Monongahela Basin

Structure Contours of the Base of the Pittsburgh Coal, Monongahela Basin

WV173 Monongahela Basin Mine Pool Project

West Virginia University Natural Resource Analysis Center

Morgantown, West Virginia, USA

By Evan Fedorko and Jerry C. Steketee

Contact
Jerry C. Steketee, jstekete@wvu.edu

Software
ArcView 3.2, Microsoft PowerPoint, Vidar TruInfo, and Windows 2000

Hardware
Dell Precision 610, Vidar Titan, and Vidar Latitude

Printer
HP DesignJet 2500CP

Data Source(s)
Various

The Monongahela and Ohio Rivers in southwestern Pennsylvania, north central West Virginia, and eastern Ohio define the Monongahela Basin. This basin contains approximately 30 coal seams of varying quality, depth, and composition. The most commercially viable seam is the Pittsburgh. The map identifies the structure contours of the Pittsburgh coal seam with the darker colors indicating greater elevation above sea level of the base of the coal seam.

The estimated total mined area of the Pittsburgh coal seam is approximately 1,600 square miles. Underground Pittsburgh coal mines appear as outlines on the map. The principal task of the GIS portion of the Mine Pool project is to gather detailed maps from state, federal, and corporate map repositories; convert them to digital georeferenced images; and digitize the mine workings. This GIS data helps to establish the location of internal and external impermeable mine barriers for predicting water flow and avoiding floods. As mining companies have folded or changed hands, barriers have been breached for man ways, haulage ways, or air and utility flow.

Many of the remaining operating mines on the Pittsburgh coal seam now extend well below the water table. To control flooding, active mines pump water into inactive mines, which have often already passively begun to fill with water. The great pressure that this water is subjected to can cause it to punch out of springs, streambeds, and riverbeds. The Mine Pool project is trying to determine the most effective way to treat the water that has filled most of these mines as well as to predict and prevent blowouts along the top of the dip.

Images of the mine maps are being used to assemble accurate polygon layers of internal mine workings as well as polygons of barriers that exist either within or between mines.

The present compilation of the Geological Map of Greece at a scale of 1:1,000,000 is based on recent geological information and the existing geological map at a scale of 1:500,000 and all geological maps at a scale of 1:50,000, which cover almost the whole Hellenic territory.

This map presents the complete geological picture of Greece, an area constituting a significant geological junction in the folded alpine arc of the Dhinarides–Hellenides–Taurides, Iranides, and other mountain ranges.

The map shows the subdivision into geotectonic zones, the lithostratigraphic succession of the geological formations including the basic tectonic structures, and specifically the nappes, which are a characteristic feature of the Hellenic mountain ranges. Younger volcanic rocks, which are related to the Aegean volcanic arc, are also recognizable within the Hellenides.

The Hellenides mountain ranges belong to the Dinaric branch. They are mainly of alpine age and were formed from the folding of formations deposited in the Tethys Ocean during the Mesozoic and Paleogene. In this area, rocks of Paleozoic and older occur that have been deformed by older folding episodes and are considered to be prealpine. There are also rocks of younger age, Lower Miocene, considered to be post-alpine excluding the molassic sediments of older age (mid-Eocene to Miocene).

Geological Map of Greece

Institute of Geology and Mineral Exploration (IGME)

Athens, Greece

By N. Androulakakis, D. Mataragas, P. Paraskevopoulos, A. Stavridis, and M. Triantafillis

Contact
N. Androulakakis, nandr@otenet.gr

Software
ArcInfo and ArcView

Hardware
Sun Ultra 5 workstation

Printer
HP DesignJet 750C

Data Source(s)
IGME

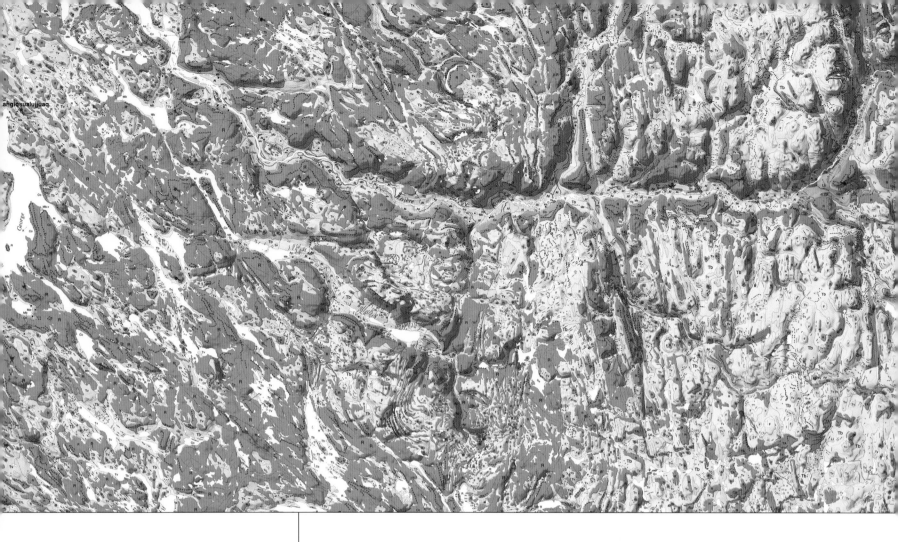

Surficial Geology—Koroc River

Natural Resources Canada, Geological Survey of Canada–Québec

Québec, Québec, Canada

By Ruth Boivin, digital cartography; Marco Boutin, photogrammetry; and Serge J. Paradis, photointerpretation

Contact

Serge J. Paradis, sparadis@nrcan.gc.ca

Software

ArcInfo, ArcGrid, and UNIX

Printer

HP DesignJet 3800CP

Data Source(s)

Geological Survey of Canada, Geomatic Canada, National Topographic Data Base, National Air Photo Library, aerial photographs, and field data

This poster was produced using A-Series maps 2013A and 2014A, which are part of a regional surficial geology mapping project financed by Natural Resources Canada through its Targeted Geoscience Initiative program.

The Geological Survey of Canada (GSC)–Québec developed a digital technique that enables the creation of modern topographic 2.5-dimensional maps using data derived directly from conventional air photos. Digital video restitution using different software coupled with ArcInfo modules enables the division to produce 2.5-dimensional or high-quality relief maps. The procedure used at GSC–Québec since 1997 has been documented and published by Natural Resources Canada, Geological Survey of Canada, Open File 4184 at www.nrcan.gc.ca/gsc/bookstore.

Plate Tectonics

About 30 million years ago, the continent of North America, riding like a ship on the heavier magma beneath, overrode the East Pacific Rise, stopping the subduction along California's west coast. The spreading energy was "transformed" along a lateral fracture of the now buried East Pacific Rise, creating the San Andreas Fault. The East Pacific Rise is still very active, running up through the Gulf of California, separating the Baja Peninsula from mainland Mexico.

Hot, molten magma from deep within the Earth rises to the surface along a narrow fracture that runs the length of the East Pacific. The new lava pushes older material away from the spreading zone, forming the East Pacific Rise. Where cooler, dense ocean crust crashes against lighter continental material, the heavier oceanic crust is subducted beneath the continents, forcing the ocean crust back into the furnace of the Earth. Some of this material melts and bubbles back up to the surface, forming the chains of volcanoes that comprise the Andes and the Central American volcanic cordillera. This same process created the Sierra Nevadas and the Peninsular Mountain Range forming the west side of the Salton Basin between 150 to 90 million years ago—the huge domes of granite the result of molten bubbles or "plutons" that hardened beneath the Earth's crust.

About 30 million years ago, the continent of North America, riding like a ship on the heavier magma beneath, overrode the East Pacific Rise, stopping the subduction along California's west coast. The spreading energy was "transformed" along a lateral fracture of the now buried East Pacific Rise, creating the San Andreas Fault. The East Pacific Rise is still very active, running up through the Gulf of California, separating the Baja Peninsula from mainland Mexico. The four volcanoes at the south end of the Salton Sea-Rock Hill, Mullet Island, Obsidian Butte, and Red Island, also known as the Salton Buttes-are evidence of the volcanic origins of the Salton Basin.

EXPLANATION

Spreading center (divergent boundary)

Subduction zone (convergent boundary)

Transform fault arrows show relative movement SAFS, San Andreas fault zone

Triple plate junction M. Mendocino R. Rivera

Process of Subduction

About 30 million years ago, the continent of North America, riding like a ship on the heavier magma beneath, overrode the East Pacific Rise, stopping the subduction along California's west coast. The spreading energy was "transformed" along a lateral fracture of the now buried East Pacific Rise, creating the San Andreas Fault. The East Pacific Rise is still very active, running up through the Gulf of California, separating the Baja Peninsula from mainland Mexico.

Subduction

Subduction of the older, heavier oceanic crust of the Pacific Plate has plunged under the crust of the North American Plate. This can create deep trenches where the plates meet.

Transform Boundary

A transform boundary is where two plates slide past each other. The San Andreas Fault is perhaps the most renowned transform fault in California.

Spreading Center

The new lava pushes older material away from the spreading zone, forming the East Pacific Rise. This spreading center and rift zone under the Gulf of California extends on land into the Salton Basin.

ESRI PRESS

This atlas is part of a series of information products designed to serve the needs of a broad stakeholder group involved in environmental planning at the Salton Sea in Southern California. While advances in scientific knowledge are tremendous, the management of natural environments benefits by a greater common understanding of these scientific principles. Relationships between the natural environment, its cultural history, and our societal values are frequently the domain of the planning expert and not part of community dialogue. This atlas, by facilitating common understanding of these complex natural and cultural systems, seeks to inform more effective and socially relevant management and policy decisions.

Focusing on the characterization of environmental change at the Salton Sea, the atlas features input and articles from a range of recognized experts, and the information is presented in an easily understood, graphically compelling, and engaging form.

You can order the atlas online from ESRI Press at www.esri.com/library/esripress or visit the Salton Sea Database Program Web site at http://cem.uor.edu/salton.

New Tools for Creating Common Understanding

University of Redlands, Redlands Institute: Salton Sea Database Program (SSDP)

Redlands, California, USA

By The Redlands Institute

Contact
Dina Guthrie, guthrie@cem.uor.edu

Software
ArcGIS, ERDAS IMAGINE, Adobe Photoshop, Adobe Illustrator, and Quark XPress

Hardware
Dell workstation

Printer
HP DesignJet 2500

Data Source(s)
SSDP, ESRI, U.S. Geological Survey, and Teale Data Center

Lake Whatcom, Bathymetric Map

City of Bellingham

Bellingham, Washington, USA

By Chris Behee

Contact

Chris Behee, cbehee@cob.org

Software

ArcGIS 8.1.2 and Windows NT

Printer

HP DesignJet 755CM

Data Source(s)

U.S. Bureau of Reclamation, U.S. Geological Survey, City of Bellingham, and Whatcom County

Lake Whatcom is a 5,000-acre glacially carved lake extending east from Bellingham into the foothills of the Cascade Mountains. Development pressure and the watershed's functions as a scenic resource, municipal water supply, recreation area, and habitat area make it a frequent subject of the local media and politics. This map was produced as part of an effort to provide effective educational tools for the public.

One of the most critical issues addressed by the maps is the relatively shallow depth of Basins 1 and 2 and their proximity to high levels of urban development. Water quality data gathered during the past 20 years shows significant levels of runoff pollutants in Basin 1 and increasing levels in Basin 2. Basin 2, from which the city draws its water supply, is under pressure for further residential development. To address this issue, local regulations are under review, and programs facilitating property acquisition and development density transfers are being explored. In July 1999, the U.S. Bureau of Reclamation conducted a bathymetric survey of Lake Whatcom to develop reservoir topography and compute area–capacity relationships, and in November of 2000, as a component of the Bureau of Reclamation efforts, the Whatcom County Public Works Department contracted to have the above-water topography mapped around the lake. This mapping effort provided two-foot contours and planimetric data for features along the shoreline to an elevation of about 320 feet (including the docks and building footprints depicted on this map).

City of Bellingham GIS staff converted the bathymetric soundings and two-foot above-water contours to a digital elevation model (DEM). The bathymetric DEM was merged with U.S. Geological Survey 10-meter resolution DEM data to create a seamless representation of bathymetric and upland areas. Shaded relief was generated using a multidirectional hillshade algorithm weighted toward a sun azimuth of 315 degrees and an illumination angle of 50 degrees above the horizon.

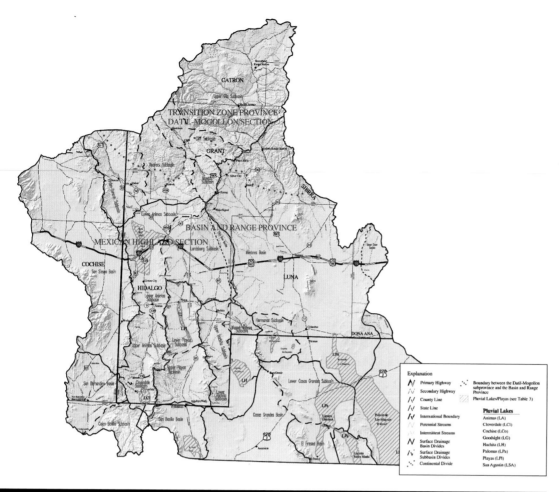

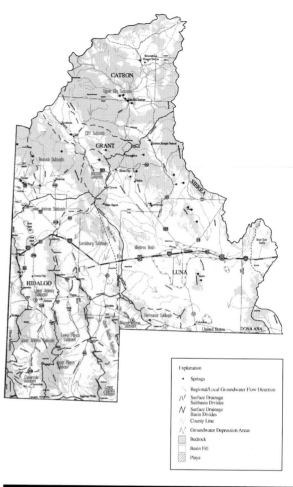

General Locations of Basins

Groundwater Flow in the Region

The New Mexico Water Resources Research Institute in cooperation with the U.S. Environmental Protection Agency has developed GIS coverages that integrate large amounts of hydrogeologic information on basin-fill aquifers in the international boundary region of southwestern New Mexico. The GIS format enables three-dimensional integration of surface and subsurface information for use in numerical groundwater flow modeling and geochemical system interpretation.

Emphasis in this presentation is on the hydrogeologic framework of five intermontane basin systems in the region west of the Mesilla Basin. From east to west, these basin systems are the Mimbres, Hachita–Moscos, Playas, Animas, and San Bernardino. The basin-fill hydrogeologic framework is defined based on composition of lithofacies assemblages (LFAs) that are organized into hydrostratigraphic units (HSUs) and the nature of basin boundary and intrabasin structural controls. Major aquifers are formed by coarser-grained LFAs associated with the ancestral Casas Grandes, Mimbres, and Animas fluvial systems. Typical horizontal hydraulic conductivities range from one to 10 meters per day, and units are usually less than 150 meters thick. Contiguous piedmont slope LFAs and underlying middle and lower Gila Group HSUs (mostly Miocene) have much lower aquifer potential because of finer matrix texture and more consolidation and cementation.

Complex half-graben basins that are linked across zones of structural accommodation have a profound effect on both local and regional groundwater flow. All basins except San Bernardino have surface flow regimes discharging to subbasins with topographic closure and playa lakes. The latter areas were sites of large perennial lakes during late Quaternary pluvial intervals. Groundwater flow in most subbasins, however, partly drains to lower contiguous basins with terminal sinks or river valleys.

Hydrogeologic Framework of Basin-Fill Aquifers in the Southwestern New Mexico Region—Integrating Framework Components Using GIS
New Mexico State University

Las Cruces, New Mexico, USA

By John F. Kennedy and John W. Hawley

Contact
John Kennedy, jkennedy@wrri.nmsu.edu

Software
ArcInfo 7.1, Solaris 2.5, and UNIX

Hardware
Sun SPARC20 workstation

Printer
HP DesignJet 750C

Data Source(s)
Surface and subsurface geology and geomorphology

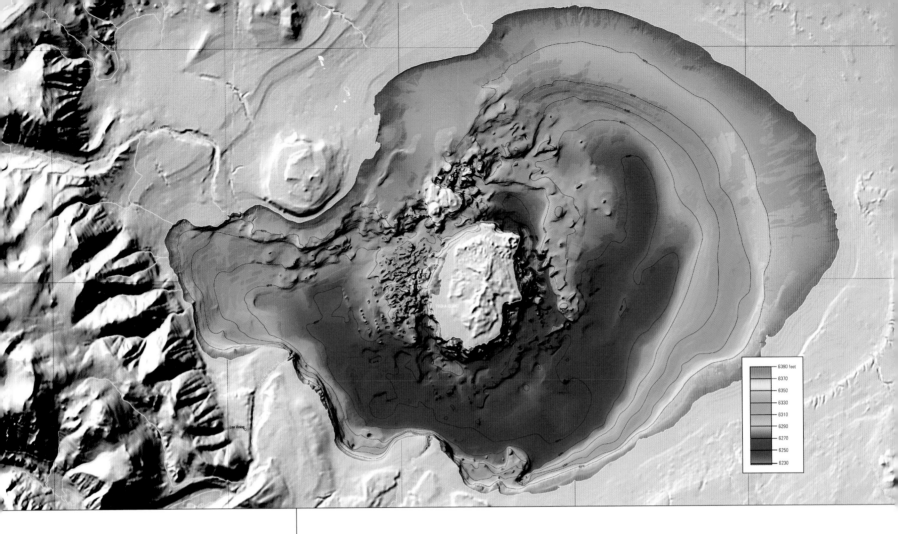

	feet
	6390
	6370
	6350
	6330
	6310
	6290
	6270
	6250
	6230

Digital Bathymetric Model of
Mono Lake, California

U.S. Geological Survey,
Western Geographic Science Center

Menlo Park, California, USA

By Alexander Evans, Christian Raumann, Scott Stine,
and Jerry Wilson

Contact
Christian Raumann, craumann@usgs.gov

Software
ArcInfo 7.2, ArcView 3.2, ERDAS IMAGINE, Adobe
Illustrator, Adobe Photoshop, and Windows NT

Printer
HP DesignJet 3500CP

Data Source(s)
U.S. Geological Survey and Pelagos Corporation

In 1986 and 1987, Pelagos Corporation of San Diego (now Racal Pelagos) undertook a bathymetric survey of Mono Lake in eastern California for the Los Angeles Department of Water and Power (DWP). The product of that survey was a series of maps at varying scales and contour intervals.

From these maps, the DWP hoped to predict consequences of the drop in lake level that resulted from the diversion of streams in the Mono Basin. No digital models, inducing shaded relief and perspective view renderings, were made from the data collected during the survey. With the permission of Pelagos Corporation and DWP, U.S. Geological Survey (USGS) used the data to produce a digital model of the floor of Mono Lake. The model was created using a GIS to incorporate the data with new observations and measurements made in the field. It should prove to be a valuable tool that will enable better visualization and analyses of the floor of Mono Lake.

More information is available from USGS Miscellaneous Field Studies Map MF-2393.

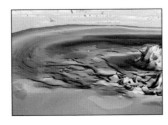

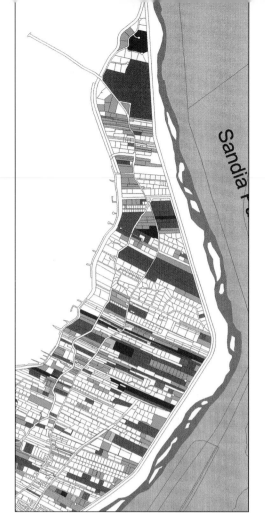

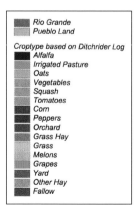

Rio Grande
Pueblo Land

Croptype based on Ditchrider Log
Alfalfa
Irrigated Pasture
Oats
Vegetables
Squash
Tomatoes
Corn
Peppers
Orchard
Grass Hay
Grass
Melons
Grapes
Yard
Other Hay
Fallow

The Middle Rio Grande Conservancy District (MRGCD), a political subdivision of the State of New Mexico, delivers water to thousands of irrigators in the middle Rio Grande Valley. The water is delivered to the fields by gravity flow through a system of canals and laterals. The service area of each ditch is tracked by MRGCD "ditchriders." These ditchriders maintain yearly logs of each field that received water including what was grown, the acreage, and the date water was delivered. Today, the MRGCD is using GIS to update and modernize these ditchrider logs. Using GIS, MRGCD can begin to distinguish between the fields the ditchriders are tracking and the fields that are actually charged for water delivery.

Last year, the MRGCD, together with the Office of the State Engineer, did a supervised classification using Space Imaging IKONOS imagery for the entire middle Rio Grande Valley. This data set was also used to identify areas that the ditchriders were missing.

Analyzing Irrigated Land in Corrales, New Mexico

Middle Rio Grande Conservancy District

Albuquerque, New Mexico, USA

By Fred Bertola, Michael Montano, DeAnna Philips, and Doug Strech

Contact
Doug Strech, dstrech@mrgcd.dst.nm.us

Software
ArcInfo 7.2.1, ArcView 3.2, ERDAS IMAGINE 8.4, and Windows NT 4.0

Printer
HP DesignJet 755CM

Data Source(s)
In-house

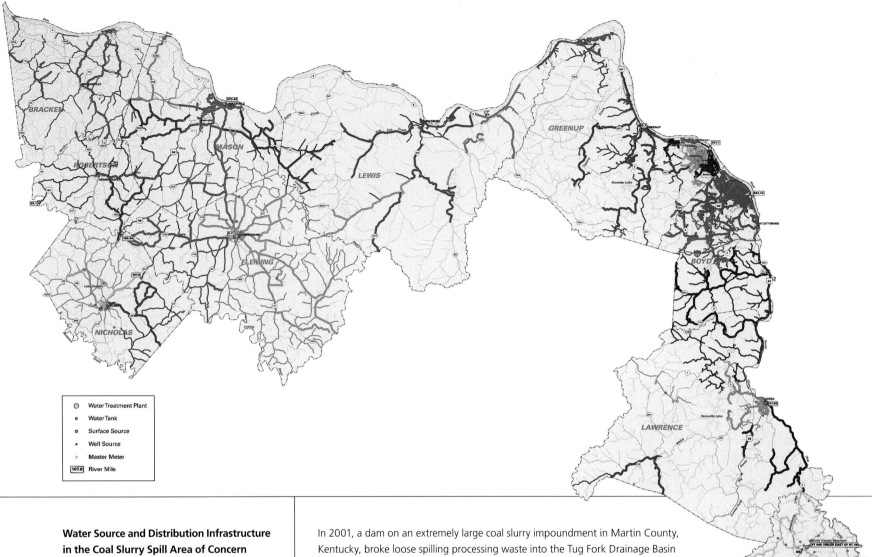

Water Source and Distribution Infrastructure in the Coal Slurry Spill Area of Concern

Natural Resources and Environmental Protection Cabinet

Frankfort, Kentucky, USA

By Kimberly and Kent Anness, Water Resource Information System

Contact
Kimberly Anness, kimberly.anness@mail.state.ky.us

Software
ArcInfo 8.0.1, ArcView 3.2a, and Macromedia Freehand 9

Hardware
Digital Server 5305, Compaq Professional workstations, and Apple PowerMac

Printer
HP DesignJet 2500CP/PS

Data Source(s)
Water Resource Information System, Natural Resources and Environmental Protection Cabinet, Kentucky Transportation Cabinet, and Kentucky Area Development Districts

In 2001, a dam on an extremely large coal slurry impoundment in Martin County, Kentucky, broke loose spilling processing waste into the Tug Fork Drainage Basin (which drains into the Ohio River). The coal processing waste slowly made its way down the Tug Fork and eventually into the Ohio River. As a part of the emergency response process, the Water Resource Information System (WRIS) at the Kentucky Infrastructure Authority was able to determine which surface and well source water systems would be impacted by the spill. Subsequently, using purchase source point information, WRIS staff were able to identify systems that purchased from other systems using the Ohio River or Tug Fork as a surface or well source.

When a list of potentially impacted systems was created, a map was generated showing their source and distribution infrastructure. The number of systems and geographic area potentially impacted by the spill was much larger than anticipated.

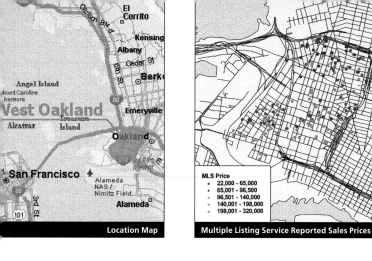

Location Map

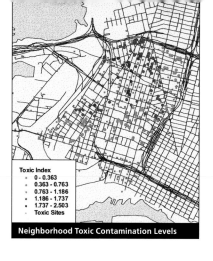

Multiple Listing Service Reported Sales Prices

MLS Price
- 22,000 - 65,000
- 65,001 - 96,500
- 96,501 - 140,000
- 140,001 - 198,000
- 198,001 - 320,000

Neighborhood Toxic Contamination Levels

Toxic Index
- 0 - 0.363
- 0.363 - 0.763
- 0.763 - 1.186
- 1.186 - 1.737
- 1.737 - 2.503
- Toxic Sites

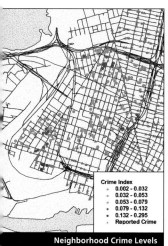

Neighborhood Crime Levels

Crime Index
- 0.002 - 0.032
- 0.032 - 0.053
- 0.053 - 0.079
- 0.079 - 0.132
- 0.132 - 0.295
- Reported Crime

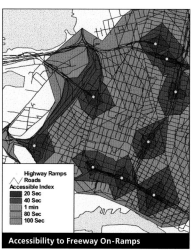

Accessibility to Freeway On-Ramps

Highway Ramps
/\ Roads
Accessible Index
- 20 Sec
- 40 Sec
- 1 min
- 80 Sec
- 100 Sec

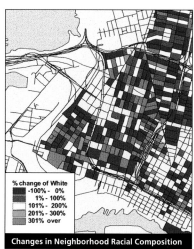

Changes in Neighborhood Racial Composition

% change of White
- -100% - 0%
- 1% - 100%
- 101% - 200%
- 201% - 300%
- 301% over

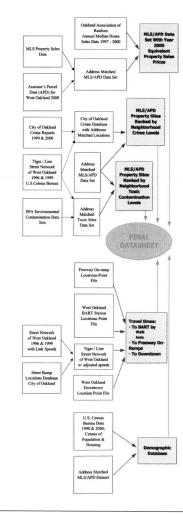

A hedonic linear regression model was constructed to predict housing values in the West Oakland area. The Institute for Urban and Regional Development at the University of California at Berkeley wanted to identify the vacant properties and environmental/toxic contamination sites in West Oakland as part of a larger effort to help West Oakland community groups improve the quality of life in their neighborhoods. This map represents a statistical model that can be used to identify the current and historical trends of development and neighborhood change in the project area and can potentially be used as a tool for guiding future community building and development activities. The hedonic price regression model predicts property values (sales prices) as a function of several selected variables such as the property characteristics, neighborhood demographics, environmental contamination, level of crime, and accessibility to jobs or services.

Model variables, such as the levels of crime and toxic contamination, the relative accessibility to employment, and the neighborhood demographic profiles of each home sold in the area from 1997–2000, were measured and input into the model. After a regression equation was calculated, it was applied to predict the value of vacant properties assuming the construction of a new single-family, two-bedroom, one-bath home at each location. This model should facilitate the evaluation of the market value of currently vacant properties and determine what factors cause price differential between properties, based on previous sales.

A test of the model was run on a group of properties in the southern area of West Oakland, near the West Oakland Bay Area Rapid Transit station. Approximately 20 toxic sties within a quarter mile of these properties were taken out of the data set to represent cleanup activities. The model predicts that the 127 vacant properties in this area would increase in value by an average of $14,000, and the total increase for all 127 vacant or recyclable properties would be roughly $1.8 million.

West Oakland Residential Development Assessment Model

University of California, Berkeley

Berkeley, California, USA

By Christopher Ferrell, Shinichiro Ikeda, Rene F. Poitevin, Julie Raffaillac, Jianchun Xu, and Demin Zhou

Contact
Jianchun Xu, xjc@gisc.berkeley.edu

Software
ArcView and Windows NT

Printer
HP DesignJet 755CM

Data Source(s)
U.S. Census Bureau and field surveys

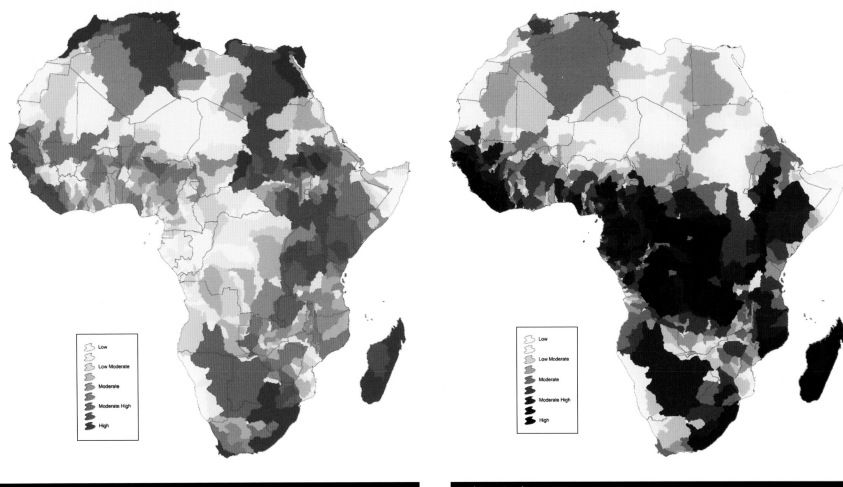

Total Water Consumption

Total Water Supply

Africa Water Balance

Earth Satellite Corporation (EarthSat)

Rockville, Maryland, USA

By Jeffrey Miller and Chris Schierkolk

Contact
Christopher Schierkolk, cschierkolk@earthsat.com

Software
ArcInfo

Printer
Symbolic Sciences Lightjet 5000 RS

Data Source(s)
ESRI, National Oceanic and Atmospheric Administration, International Geosphere–Biosphere Programme, World Resources Institute, Oak Ridge National Laboratory, U.S. Geological Survey, World Bank, and United Nations Food and Agriculture Organization

Earth Satellite Corporation collaborated with ISCIENCES to develop a GIS that assesses food and water balances at regional scales. Iterative processes and flow models are applied to map food and water supply, demand, and balance to identify chronic problem areas across the entire African continent.

Water Balance
The Africa water balance GIS model draws the total average annual water demand from the total average annual renewable water supply to estimate the regional watershed water balance.

Interwatershed flow is modeled to produce an end-state water balance. This is water balance in which water has flowed through the drainage network and reached its final destination. Throughout the course of flow, water balance is drawn down by local demand.

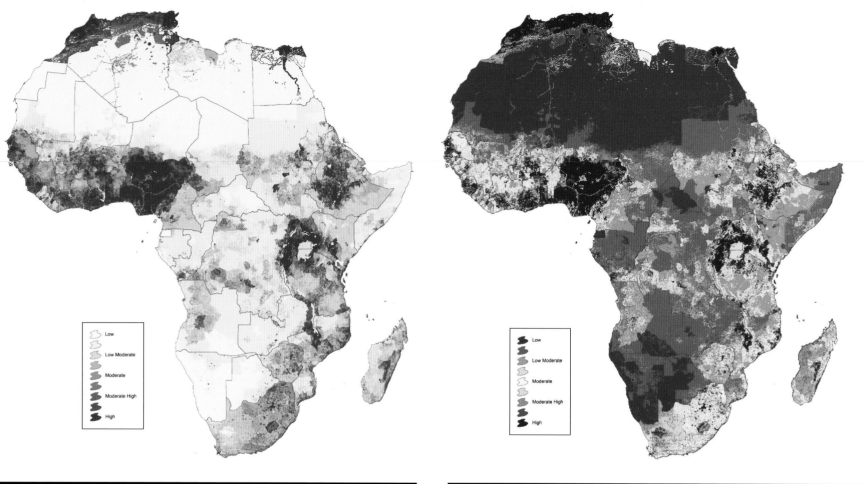

Total Food Demand

Total Food Supply

Low
Low Moderate
Moderate
Moderate High
High

Low
Low Moderate
Moderate
Moderate High
High

Food Balance

The Africa food balance model is a supply, demand, and balance GIS process. Total food supply is the sum of food imports and domestic food production from the 1998 United Nations Food and Agriculture Organization Statistical Databases (FAOSTAT) estimates. Food production is mapped through GIS allocation of national food imports to a suitability surface based on cost distance to import centers, population density, agricultural primeness, and the concentration of domestic wealth.

The food demand surface maps daily caloric consumption per square kilometer throughout Africa. Food demand is subtracted from food supply to derive an estimate food balance, showing areas of surplus and shortage throughout the continent. FAOSTAT 1998 domestic and import food production is allocated through a multicriteria model to produce domestic and import calorie supply surfaces.

Africa Food Balance

Earth Satellite Corporation (EarthSat)

Rockville, Maryland, USA

By Jeffrey Miller and Chris Schierkolk

Contact

Christopher Schierkolk, cschierkolk@earthsat.com

Software

ArcInfo

Printer

Symbolic Sciences Lightjet 5000 RS

Data Source(s)

ESRI, National Oceanic and Atmospheric Administration, International Geosphere–Biosphere Programme, World Resources Institute, Oak Ridge National Laboratory, U.S. Geological Survey, World Bank, and United Nations Food and Agriculture Organization

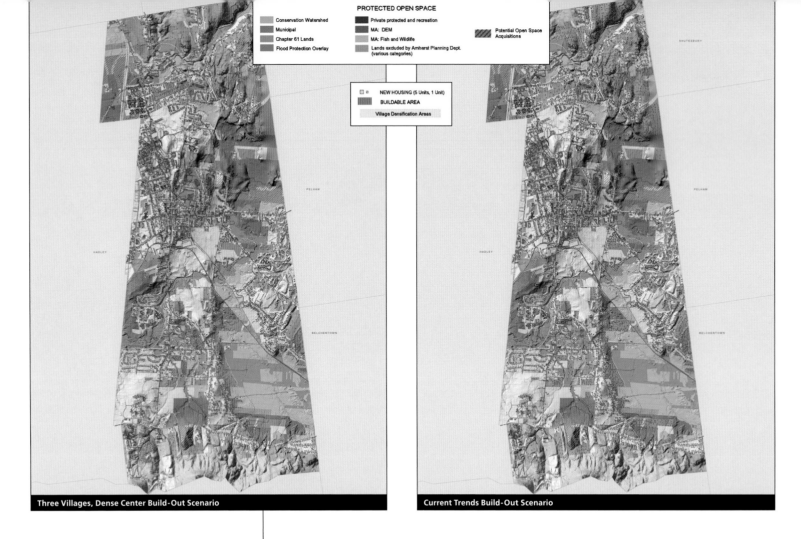

PROTECTED OPEN SPACE

Conservation Watershed	Private protected and recreation
Municipal	MA: DEM
Chapter 61 Lands	MA: Fish and Wildlife
Flood Protection Overlay	Lands excluded by Amherst Planning Dept. (various categories)

Potential Open Space Acquisitions

NEW HOUSING (5 Units, 1 Unit)
BUILDABLE AREA
Village Densification Areas

Three Villages, Dense Center Build-Out Scenario

Current Trends Build-Out Scenario

Potential Build-Out Scenarios—
Amherst, Massachusetts

Applied Geographics, Inc.

Boston, Massachusetts, USA

By Philip B. Herr and Richard Sutton

Contact
Richard Sutton, rs@appgeo.com

Software
ArcMap 8.1, Visual Basic-enhanced Microsoft Excel, and Windows 2000 5.0

Hardware
Dell OptiPlex GX200

Printer
HP DesignJet 1050

Data Source(s)
Various

This map portrays buildable land in the town of Amherst, Massachusetts. Amherst contracted with Applied Geographics, Inc. (AGI), and Philip B. Herr & Associates to conduct a townwide Build-Out Analysis and Future Growth Study. The town, with a population of approximately 35,000, is home to Amherst College, Hampshire College, and the University of Massachusetts and is subject to a unique combination of development pressures.

AGI created a composite of total developable land by aggregating more than two dozen constraints layers including wetlands, aquifer protection areas, river protection buffers, steep slopes, conservation parcels, municipal properties, and lands currently developed to legal density limits. These constraints were combined with a current zoning layer to quantify total developable land by district. Zoning bylaws and constraints variables were carefully assembled in cooperation with town officials and planning committee members and factored against the developable land geometry to generate total additional population and resource loads for the town at full build-out. These included values for additional total and student populations, dwelling units, residential and commercial water consumption, solid waste production, and new road construction.

In addition, AGI worked with the town to generate multiple development scenarios to evaluate attainment of these build-out totals. This required crafting parcel-specific combinations of development densification and new open space acquisition. Individual points for new dwelling units were placed according to allowable zoning density requirements and their locations fine-tuned to accommodate assumptions of the varying scenarios. The results were presented to the public for commentary, discussion, and markup. Many of the project materials and analysis products are available on the Web at www.appgeo.com/clients/amherst.

Change in city population during 10-year period:

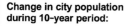

- Increase > 10 %
- Increase 2 – 10 %
- Stable (± 1 %)
- Decrease 2 – 10 %
- Decrease > 10 %
- Data not available

This map was created within the INTERREG II C research project, Urban Systems and Urban Networking in the Baltic Sea Region, for the Committee for Spatial Development in the Baltic Sea Region (CSD/BSR). It contributed to the Vision and Strategies Around the Baltic Sea 2010 (VASAB) 2010 PLUS Spatial Development Action Programme. VASAB is a collaboration of spatial planning and development ministers from countries around the Baltic Sea.

The map depicts the change in city population during the 1990s. Because of data inavailability, the exact time frame differs slightly from country to country but generally refers to the period 1989–1998. During the last decade, political and structural economic changes have altered the settlement pattern around the Baltic Sea dramatically. This is true for both transition and traditional market economy countries. The region is heterogeneous, and no joint pattern emerges. The development of urban population is guided largely by different stages of the urbanization process that each country is in. Three main scenarios emerge. There has been a substantial population decline in the cities of northwest Russia, in virtually all Estonian and Latvian cities, and in northeastern Germany (Mecklenburg–Vorpommern, Brandenburg). This corresponds with the structural changes that have occurred after the shift to market economy.

There is a substantial growth in certain areas with smaller settlements surrounding larger cities indicating continued urban sprawl, and there are large cities that have grown at a dramatic pace during the decade, mainly in Belarus, Finland, Norway, and Sweden. The Nordic capitals apart from Copenhagen are among the 10 fastest growing regions in Western Europe.

Population Change in Baltic Sea Region Cities with More Than 10,000 Inhabitants, 1990s

Nordregio–Nordic Centre for Spatial Development

Stockholm, Sweden

By Tomas Hanell and Jörg Neubauer

Contact
Tomas Hanell, tomas.hanell@nordregio.se

Software
ArcView 3.2

Hardware
Dell Precision 220 workstation

Printer
HP Color LaserJet 5

Data Source(s)
Ministry of Statistics and Analysis (Belarus), Statistics Denmark, Statistical Office of Estonia, Statistics Finland, Federal Statistical Office (Germany), Central Statistical Bureau of Latvia, Department of Statistics to the Government of the Republic of Lithuania, Statistics Norway, GUS–Polish Official Statistics, State Committee of the Russian Federation on Statistics (Goskomstat), Statistics Sweden, regional statistical institutes in the Russian Federation, Eurostat, Nordregio, and ESRI

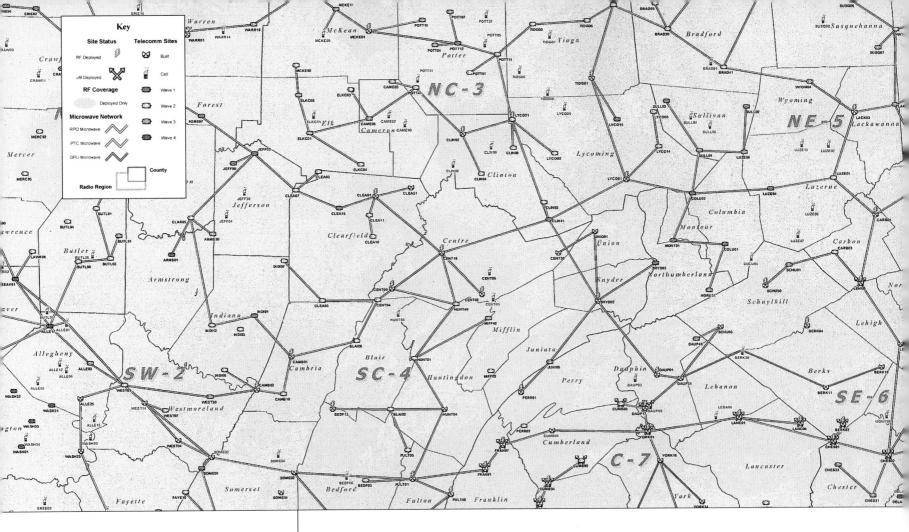

Commonwealth of Pennsylvania Example
Radio Project System and Status

RCC Consultants, Inc. (RCC)

Woodbridge, New Jersey, USA

By Pete Wilkins

Contact
Terry Wright, comsite.esri@rcc.com

Software
ArcGIS 8.2, ArcView 3.2, ComSiteDesign, and
Windows NT

Printer
HP DesignJet 750

Data Source(s)
ESRI; Geographic Data Technology, Inc.;
Pennsylvania Spatial Data Access; and RCC

A major step in telecommunication system design is determining signal coverage whether it is for existing sites or future build-out locations. Radio frequency engineers use ComSiteDesign, an RCC Consultants, Inc., product, to generate propagation coverage footprints. The propagation parameters are based on industry-standard models as well as site and sector/antenna details depending on individual client needs or specifications. These coverage areas are then exported to ArcView shapefiles, which can then be used in detailed geographic analysis.

GIS analysts use the coverage shapefiles to conduct detailed spatial overlay analysis depending on a client's requirements. Analyses can include demographics for future site planning or Federal Communications Commission (FCC) licensing requirements, signal redundancy for minimum build-out or contingency coverage, GPS-based field measurements to quality control and assurance propagation parameters, and locating operators within FCC licensing areas to focus marketing strategies.

Results can be incorporated into designs for an integrated communication network using multiple technologies. By combining the radio frequency propagation prediction models and the GIS analysis capabilities, telecommunication companies can effectively design, implement, and maintain entire systems ranging from local to statewide to regional. This leads to improved system integration, connectivity, and reliability while at the same time lowering building costs, providing maximum customer service, and planning future developments.

This map represents a conceptual partial deployment and is not indicative of a final network design.

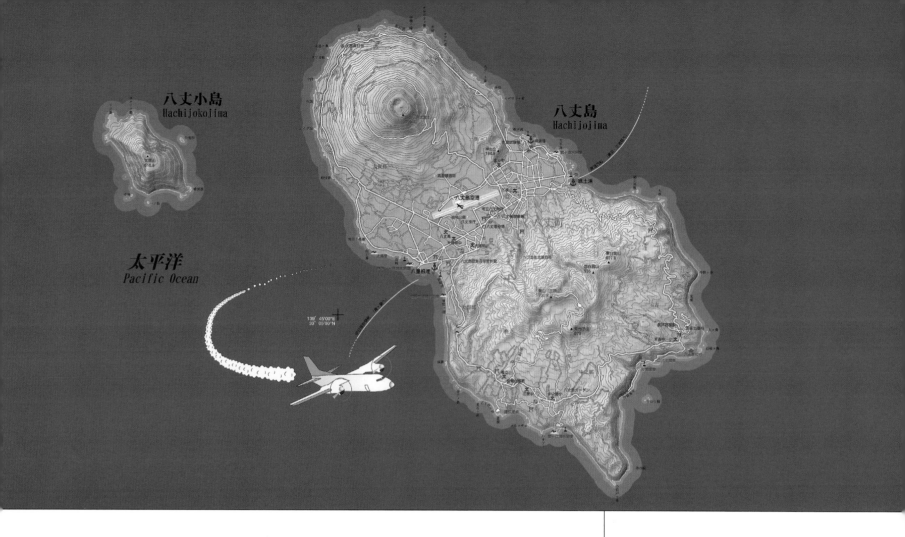

This poster shows a tourist map of Hachijojima, an island located approximately 290 kilometers south of Tokyo, Japan, in the Izu-Ogasawara (Bonin) group. Hachijojima is a volcanic island and consists of Mt. Higashi (701 meters) and Mt. Nishi (854 meters). The circumference of the island is roughly 59 kilometers, and it covers 62.3 square kilometers. Mt. Higashi is an inactive volcano, but Mt. Nishi last erupted in 1707.

This map was created specifically with color contrast to show the beautiful shape of the island, which was created by the volcanic mountains. The ArcInfo Buffer function was used for the coastal areas, which makes the island appear to be floating on the ocean. The ArcGrid module made the illuminated relief with layer tinting.

The elevation data is based on 50-meter digital elevation model data published by the Geographical Survey Institute of Japan. Other map data is based on research from Yumekoubou Co., Ltd. This data was edited with ArcInfo 8.0.2 with the layout arranged to graphic metafile with ArcPlot. Vector data was converted to Illustrator format and raster data was converted to Encapsulated PostScript format using ArcInfo. This was edited in Adobe Illustrator version 8.0.1 for Japanese.

Island Map—Hachijojima, Izu, Ogasawara (Bonin) Islands
Yumekoubou Co., Ltd.

Tokyo, Japan

By Go Ishikawa

Contact
Go Ishikawa, ishikawa@yumeya.co.jp

Software
ArcInfo 8.0.2 for UNIX, ArcGrid, and Adobe Illustrator 8J for Macintosh

Hardware
Sun Ultra 30 and PowerMac G4

Printer
Offset press

Data Source(s)
Geographical Survey Institute technology and custom data

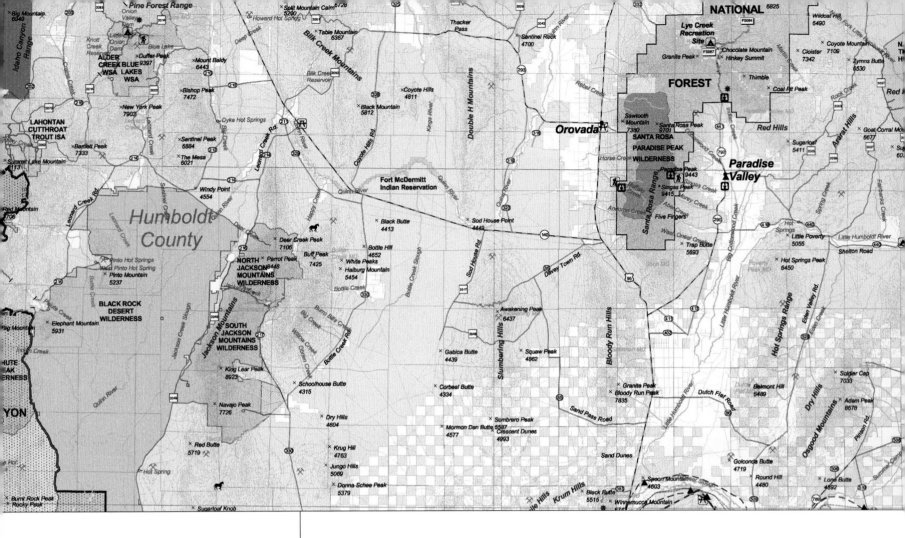

Nevada Winnemucca Recreation Guide

U.S. Department of the Interior, Bureau of Land Management (BLM)

Winnemucca, Nevada, USA

By Rick Crawford

Contact
Rick Crawford, rick_crawford@fs.fed.us

Software
ArcView 3.2 and Windows NT

Printer
HP DesignJet 755CM

Data Source(s)
BLM

This map is a working copy of a map from the Bureau of Land Management (BLM), Nevada, *Northwestern Recreation Guide,* which was published in September 2001. The map is two-sided with the north half on the front and the south half on the back. The BLM offices in northern Nevada (Winnemucca and Reno) sell copies of the map, and it is available online in PDF format at www.nv.blm.gov/winnemucca/recreation.

This map is a guide for visitors to the public lands of northern Nevada. The area of the map includes lands that in December 1999 were designated as a National Conservation Area (NCA) such as the Black Rock Desert–High Rock Canyon Emigrant Trails National Conservation Area. Ten wilderness areas also are associated with the NCA.

A GIS maintained by the BLM Winnemucca Field Office was used to generate the map. For this map and the Web version, the text was inserted into text blocks in the layout, and the map was printed on a plotter for the hard copy. The version of the map that later went to publication was exported to PostScript without the text blocks. The map was imported into an image processor where each of the colors was isolated and converted to CMYK values. Two PostScript images were sent to the printer—one with the map and the other with the text—and were superimposed at the time of printing. For the first printing, 10,000 copies were made. The BLM hopes to update the map before each new printing.

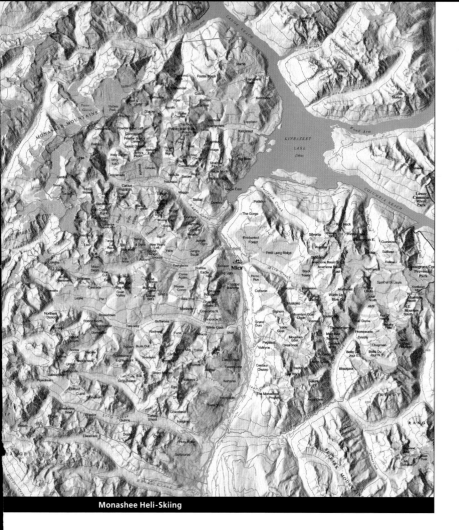

Monashee Heli-Skiing

Revelstoke Heli-Skiing

Canadian Mountain Holiday (CMH) has been offering the ultimate deep powder skiing experience in 15,765 square kilometers of remote and spectacular mountain settings for more than 30 years. As the world's first and largest helicopter skiing operator, CMH wanted to offer its clients a unique memento of their adventure holiday and asked Clover Point Cartographics to create a series of posters for each of their 11 operating areas.

The posters are based on the operational base maps used daily by CMH planners and guides. These base maps, created by Clover Point Cartographics in 1999, are composed of 1:20,000 topographic features, a digital elevation model (DEM), and CMH operational layers (tenure areas, ski runs, helicopter pickup/drop-off sites, lodges, and safety caches). The background hillshade was generated from a 20-meter DEM. To maximize effectiveness, the lattice tiles for each of the more than 200 1:20,000 map sheets were converted to points, clipped, and appended before creating a triangulated irregular network (TIN). The TIN was converted back to a lattice, filtered, and used to generate a hillshade showing no evidence of the original map sheet edges. The hillshade was brought into ArcView as an image rather than a grid, enabling the manipulation of contrast and brightness.

Print files created from ArcView were sent directly to a commercial printer who was able to economically print the thousands of copies required. Each area manager had slightly different ideas for the posters such as emphasizing the mountaintops. For this, the cartographic team hid the hillshade behind an elevation shading for selected elevation areas. While most managers wished to show ski runs as areas, some elected to show runs as lines, underscoring the temporary, minimal footprint they leave on the terrain. The posters were produced at a variety of scales because each operating area is a different size and all had to fit within the same poster dimension.

**Canadian Mountain Holidays—
Hiking, Mountaineering, and Skiing**
Clover Point Cartographics Ltd.

Victoria, British Columbia, Canada

By Kathleen Lush

Contact
David Nicolson, dave.n@cloverpoint.com

Software
ArcInfo 8.0.2, ArcView 3.2, ArcView Spatial Analyst, and Windows NT

Printer
HP DesignJet 1055CM

Data Source(s)
British Columbia Terrain Resource Information Management Program and Canadian Mountain Holidays

Clover Point Cartographics Ltd.

**Santorini (Thira) Island,
Aegean Islands, Greece**

Anavasi Editions

Athens, Greece

By Triantafyllos Adamakopoulos
and Penelope Matsouka

Contact
Penelope Matsouka, info@mountains.gr

Software
ArcView 3.2, ArcPad™, and CorelDraw

Hardware
Athlon class computers, laptop, palmtop, and global
positioning system unit

Printer
Offset printer

Data Source(s)
Various

The island of Santorini (Thira) is perhaps the most
striking of the cylcadic islands of the Aegean Sea.
Arising out of lava that solidified around primordial
limestone cores, the island complex of Santorini has
changed form many times in recent geological periods.

The maps of the Hellenic Army Geographical Service at 1:50,000 scale
are the basic source of the topographic and thematic data. Existing data was recorded in the GIS, while topographical data was interpreted and digitized. Supplementary and other data relevant to the relief, such as
the river network, were also digitized and used to construct a digital elevation model of the area. For maps
intended for use in the field, the portrayal of the relief must be both graphic and comprehensive. Three different methods were combined for a cartographic reproduction of the relief—contour intervals, altitude zones of
different colors, and techniques of shaded relief. Another important point in the process was communication
with locals to ensure accurate place names and locate other elements in the region. Field research was done
with GPS receivers and a laptop computer (in vehicles) or a palmtop (while on foot). This map is part of an
ongoing project to compile a large geographic database for the whole of Greece.

Anavasi Editions

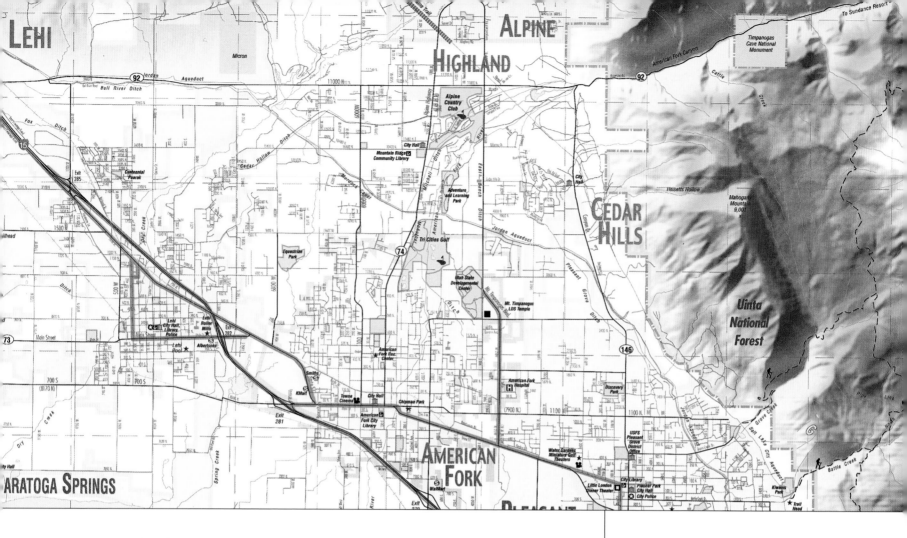

This map shows bicycle routes, bus routes, area attractions, recreational facilities, and other points of interest. The presentation also includes information on proper use of bikes in traffic and public transportation alternatives.

Utah Valley Bike, Walk, and Bus Guide
Mountainland Association of Governments

Orem, Utah, USA

By Mike Nelson and Andrew Wooley

Contact
Andrew Wooley, awooley@mountainland.org

Software
ArcMap, Macromedia Freehand, and Windows 2000

Printer
Print Shop

Data Source(s)
Mountainland Association of Governments and Utah County Public Works

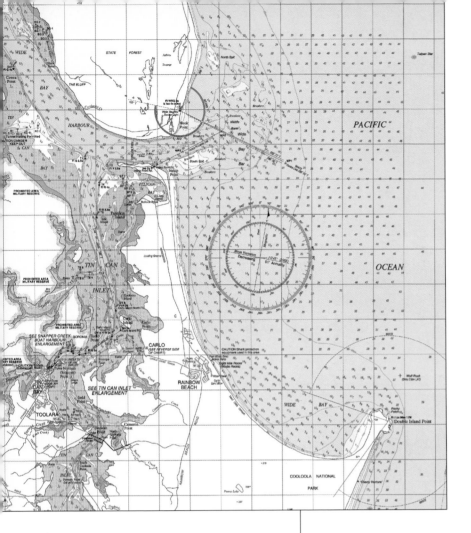

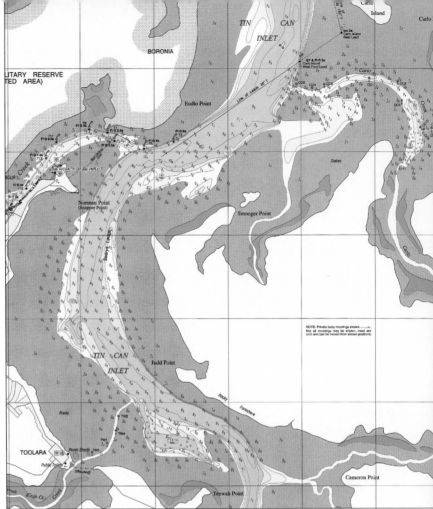

Great Sandy Strait (South) Boating Safety Chart

Queensland Transport, Maritime Division, Marine Cartography and GIS Unit

Brisbane, Queensland, Australia

By Wayne Bagnell, Vicki Langton, Anne Shaw, John Thomas, and Shirley Webb

Contact

Wayne Bagnell, wayne.m.bagnell@transport.qld.gov.au

Software

ArcInfo, ArcEdit, ArcPlot, and UNIX

Hardware

Sun workstations

Printer

Offset printer

Data Source(s)

Various

The Maritime Division of Queensland Transport has four broad functions—to ensure marine safety, reduce and mitigate ship-sourced pollution, promote and manage sustainable use of Queensland waters, and develop the maritime industry. As part of these functions, one of its activities is publishing local nautical charts for the boating community. A series of boating safety charts has been issued since the 1950s, and until recently, they were prepared manually. The charts are full navigation nautical charts conforming to international standards with some symbol modifications for small craft users in Queensland waters. In 1998, the first boating safety chart was published directly from ArcInfo software.

The Great Sandy Strait Boating Safety chart is the seventh map produced digitally direct from ArcInfo. The Great Sandy Strait lies between mainland Queensland and Fraser Island. It is a popular waterway for recreational boating and coastal yachts. Much of the chart information has been digitized or manually entered into the ArcInfo GIS from existing charts. New hydrographic surveys were captured into ArcEdit from the hydrographic CAD system by exporting soundings as ASCII files and contours as DXF. The entire chart, including symbols, legend layouts, insets, and bit maps, is compiled in ArcInfo using ARC Macro Language. Atools were written to help conform to the labeling conventions for soundings, compass roses, legends, and symbol layouts.

A list of all boating safety charts is online at the Queensland Transport Web site (www.transport.qld.gov.au) under Maritime. These maps placed second in the Best Cartographic Design category at ESRI's 2001 International User Conference.

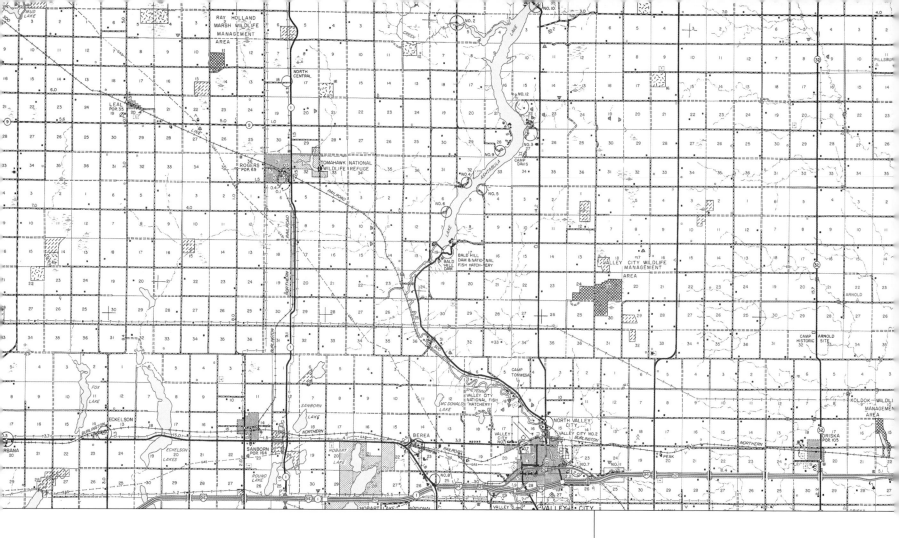

For 70 years, the North Dakota Department of Transportation (NDDOT) has been producing County General Highway maps. Map production has evolved from a pen-and-ink process drafted on linen to digital. With a desire to be able to supply timely map information to highway planners and design personnel, NDDOT began the process of converting to electronic versions that duplicated the same look and feel as the existing hand-produced maps.

Existing maps were digitized into ArcInfo coverages over several years. During this time, symbols and line types were built to replicate the exiting maps. The setup process is complete along with all necessary symbology for the county maps. The finished electronic maps contain three or more views with up to 20 different map extents used per layout. The first electronic County General Highway map was commercially printed in the spring of 2001.

General Highway Map, Barnes County
North Dakota Department of Transportation (NDDOT)

Bismarck, North Dakota, USA

By Pam Lannoye, Steven Nelson, and Roger Roehl

Contact
Roger Roehl, rroehl@state.nd.us

Software
ArcInfo 7.2, ArcView 3.2, and Windows NT

Printer
Offset press

Data Source(s)
NDDOT and various local governments

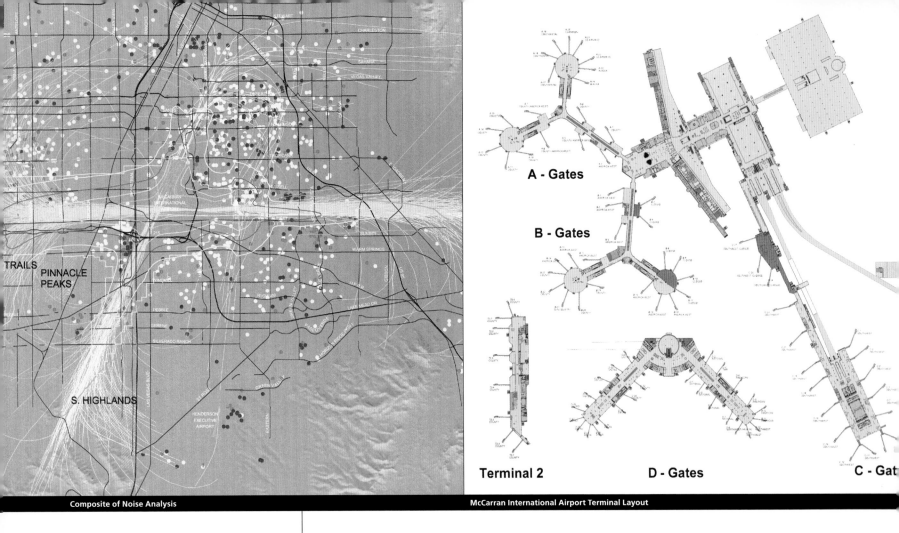

TRAILS PINNACLE PEAKS

S. HIGHLANDS

HENDERSON EXECUTIVE AIRPORT

GREEN VALLEY

A - Gates

B - Gates

Terminal 2

D - Gates

C - Gat

Composite of Noise Analysis

McCarran International Airport Terminal Layout

McCarran International Airport

Clark County Department of Aviation

Las Vegas, Nevada, USA

By Majed Khater *(Terminal Layout)* and Sonya Wilson
(Noise Analysis)

Contact

Majed Khater, mak@mccarran.com
Sonya Wilson, swn@mccarran.com

Software

ArcInfo 8.1 *(Terminal Layout),* ArcInfo 7.2,
ArcView 3.x *(Noise Analysis),* and Windows NT 4.0

Printer

HP DesignJet 1050C

Data Source(s)

Various

McCarran International Airport Terminal Layout

This map shows the terminal layout at McCarran International Airport in Las Vegas. It includes all of the main terminal buildings, gate cluster buildings, parking structures, and tramways. The seventh busiest airport in the country and the eleventh busiest worldwide, McCarran uses GIS to track relevant data as it pertains to the terminal layout including leased space, amenities, gate organization, and other facility data. The airport layout in GIS is a valuable tool to assist airport staff with current and proposed projects, data and graphic needs, and other requests that affect day-to-day operations of the airport. The data used in the map was initially converted from AutoCAD to GIS and then maintained and updated using ArcInfo. Internal staff use this data in a desktop application called Terminal Management System, which is also linked to other relevant facility data for enhanced functionality. This application integrates MapObjects and ArcSDE layers to provide a seamless view of the terminal data with zoom and query capabilities.

Composite of Noise Analysis

This map shows a variety of data as it relates to noise at the airports in Las Vegas, Nevada. The base image is a relief file of Las Vegas Valley done by a hillshade draped over digital elevation model data. The map depicts a typical week of aircraft radar flight tracks, encompassing arrival, departure, and training operations for McCarran International Airport, North Las Vegas Airport, and Henderson Executive Airport. An address-matched database of known noise complaints from 1991 to 2000 is also shown. This map shows the correlation of noise complaints over time to the known areas of high aircraft noise. The ability to map this data with GIS over time enables airport managers to analyze the effects of air traffic and resulting noise impacts, and it can be used to assist with developing air traffic patterns and policies that are compatible with noise-sensitive land development. Multiple airport operations can be managed more effectively complying with the Federal Aviation Administration's published rules and procedures while attempting to minimize noise impacts.

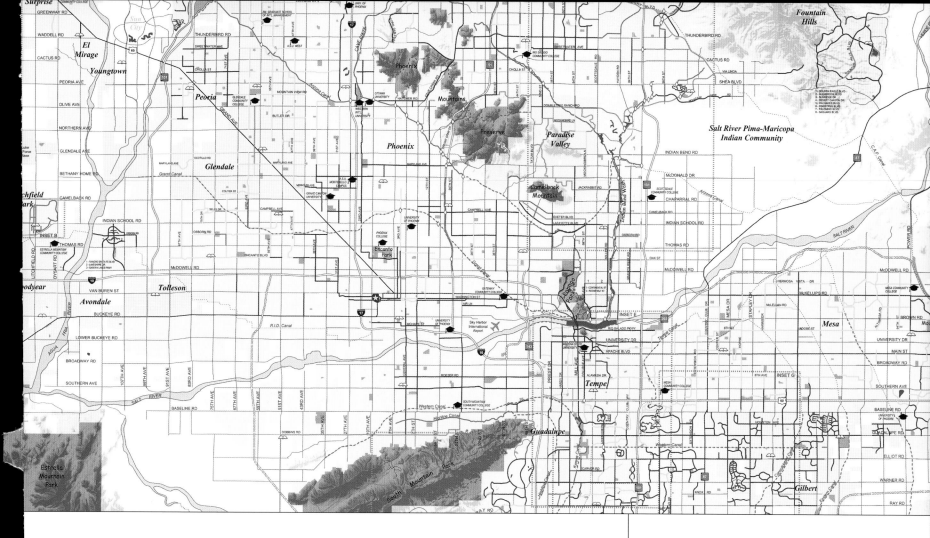

This map shows existing, locally designated bicycle facilities and was produced for free distribution by the Maricopa Association of Governments (MAG) under the direction of the MAG Regional Bicycle Task Force. It was prepared to aid bicyclists in the metropolitan Phoenix region. Data on locally designated bicycle facilities was collected from MAG member agencies and cumulated to create a regionwide map that shows both paved and unpaved bicycle paths and trails.

Bikeways

Maricopa Association of Governments (MAG)

Phoenix, Arizona, USA

By Chris Bruce and Gordon Tyus

Contact
Chris Bruce, cbruce@mag.maricopa.gov

Software
ArcInfo 8.0.2, Adobe PageMaker, and
Windows 2000

Data Source(s)
MAG GIS database

Maricopa Association of Governments

California State Highway Map

California Department of Transportation (Caltrans)

Sacramento, California, USA

By Office of Highway System Engineering, Caltrans; Office of GIS, Caltrans; and Geographic Information Center, California State University, Chico

Contact
Daniel E. Cherry, daniel.cherry@dot.ca.gov

Software
ArcInfo 7.2.1, ArcView 3.2a, Adobe Illustrator, UNIX, and Windows NT

Hardware
HP workstations

Printer
SciTex laser film image setter and Miller 40-inch, 6-color printing press

Data Source(s)
Caltrans Spatial Data Library

The California State Highway map is a cartographic product displaying the existing, planned, and proposed state highways. The map contains 32 insets that provide more detail on specific areas. Historically, California Department of Transportation (Caltrans) cartographers would hand-scribe base maps. The base maps were used to print the final maps by standard lithographic techniques. Caltrans changed the process by using GIS for the 2000 edition.

A specialized ArcView project was created to assist in quality assurance. Caltrans contracted to have the final maps produced. The GIS information was assembled in publication software along with annotation, and the final maps were produced with standard lithographic techniques.

California Department of Transportation

Existing Land Use, 1995

Agriculture
Commercial/Retail
Estate Residential
High-Density Residential
Heavy Industrial
Institutional/Public
Low-Density Residential
Light Industrial
Multifamily Residential

Medium-Density Residential
Mixed Manufacturing/Industrial
Office/Professional
Park/Recreation
Right-of-Way
Transportation/Utilities
Vacant
Water

Future Land Use, 2020

Agriculture
Commercial/Retail
High Density Residential
Heavy Industrial
Institutional/Public
Low-Density Residential
Light Industrial

Medium-Density Residential
Office/Distribution
Office/Professional
Park/Recreation
Right-of-Way
Transportation/Utilities
Water

The purpose of the GIS analysis was to proportion census tract level household and employment information to the Transportation Analysis Zone (TAZ) level for input into travel demand forecasting models used in the Gwinnett County Comprehensive Transportation Plan. A TAZ is a special area delineated by state and/or local transportation officials for tabulating traffic-related data such as journey-to-work and place-of-work statistics. A TAZ usually consists of one or more census blocks, block groups, or census tracts. Additional analyses included the calculation of household and employment densities to determine the feasibility and location of transit options.

For the analysis, 1995 was chosen as the base year. Updates to the existing 1990 household data, employment data, and TAZ boundaries were required for modeling purposes. First, control totals for 1995 household and employment data were established, and then TAZs that were to remain unchanged and new TAZs were identified (based on existing land use). Original TAZs were referred to as parent TAZs. Household and employment data was carried forward to unchanged TAZs. Estimates on the number of households or employment for each acre of land use were established. For each TAZ, acres of existing land uses were summarized, and the number of households and employment totals were proportioned into each new TAZ. Households and employment totals were checked against the control totals, and individual TAZ totals were adjusted as needed.

The GIS analysis created an efficient process for allocation of household and employment statistics by TAZ although some manual adjustments were still required. Household and employment densities were insufficient to support many transit options for the county.

Gwinnett County Transportation Plan
EDAW

Atlanta, Georgia, USA

By Patrick Peters

Contact
Patrick Peters, petersp@edaw.com

Software
ArcView 3.2 and Windows NT

Printer
HP DesignJet 755CM

Data Source(s)
U.S. Census Bureau, Atlanta Regional Commission, Georgia GIS Clearinghouse, and Gwinnett County

EDAW

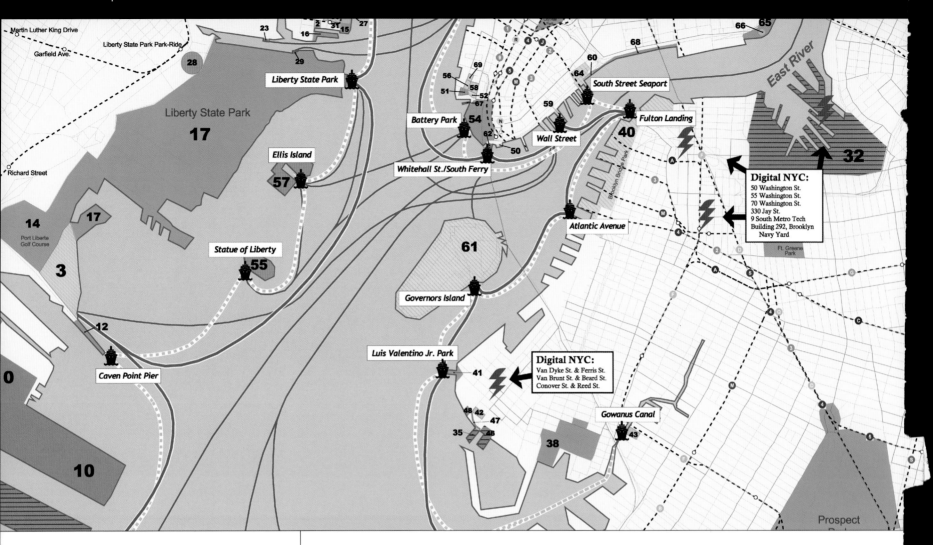

Harbor Loop Ferry

New York Public Interest Research Group Community
Mapping Assistance Project

New York, New York, USA

By Christy Knight

Contact

Steven Romalewski, sromalewski@nypirg.org

Software

ArcInfo 8.0.1, ArcView 3.2a, and Windows NT 4.0

Printer

HP DesignJet 2500CP

Data Source(s)

Metropolitan Waterfront Alliance, New York City
Planning Dept., New York City Transit, and U.S.
Census Bureau

The bay where the Hudson River meets the ocean is home to international landmarks, such as the Statue of Liberty and Ellis Island, and is a hub of the region's shipping and transportation network. Dozens of development projects are now underway. More than seven million square feet of office space, 3,000 units of housing, 1,000 hotel rooms, and the expansion of 13 different cultural attractions total nearly $2 billion in new construction. At the same time, redevelopment of many of the remaining sites, including the four largest tracts—Governors Island, Ellis Island, Homeport/Stapleton, the Military Ocean Terminal Bayonne—is thwarted by poor transportation access.

The Metropolitan Waterfront Alliance (www.waterwire.net), a network dedicated to reclaiming and reconnecting to the harbor, rivers, and estuaries of the New York and New Jersey waterfront, came to the New York Public Interest Research Group (NYPIRG) Community Mapping Assistance Project (CMAP) for help with its Harbor Loop Proposal. The project calls for the creation of 15 new ferry stops, which will enhance regional mobility; improve the quality of life in communities underserved by transit; and create new work, living, and recreational opportunities for current and future residents of the region. This proposal is a crucial first step in providing improved access and a new transportation alternative for Upper New York Bay, the crossroads of the metropolitan region, especially as New York rebuilds in the aftermath of September 11. NYPIRGCMAP's Web site is at www.nonprofitmaps.org.

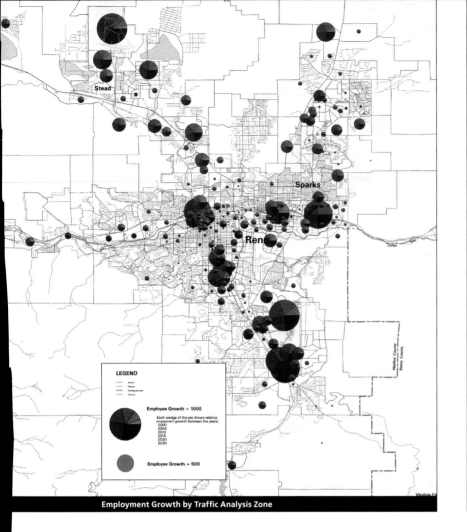

Employment Growth by Traffic Analysis Zone

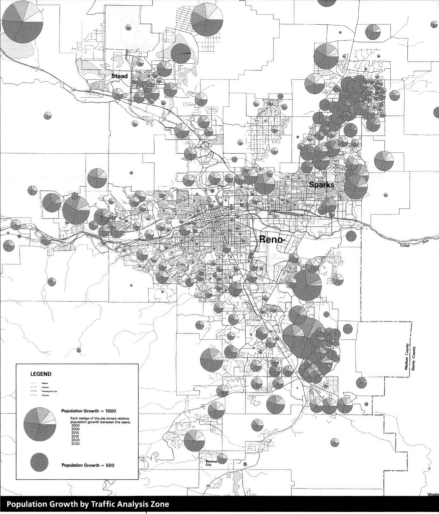

Population Growth by Traffic Analysis Zone

These maps demonstrate the use of relative-sized dots for displaying growth. The residential population and number of employees for various years were established for each traffic analysis zone in Washoe County, Nevada. The population and employment growth were determined by calculating the difference in the population between the years 2010 and 2000 and the years 2020 and 2000. The same was done for the number of employees.

Population growth and employment growth are symbolized with different colored dots. Displaying dots for both residential and employment growth on the same map shows that in most areas, population growth will exceed employment growth—a potential traffic problem.

Population Growth and Employment Growth

Parsons Corporation

San Jose, California, USA

By Eric Coumou

Contact
Eric Coumou, eric.coumou@parsons.com

Software
ArcInfo

Printer
HP DesignJet 1050

Data Source(s)
Clark County Planning Department, Washoe County Planning Department, and Parsons Transportation Group

Parsons Corporation

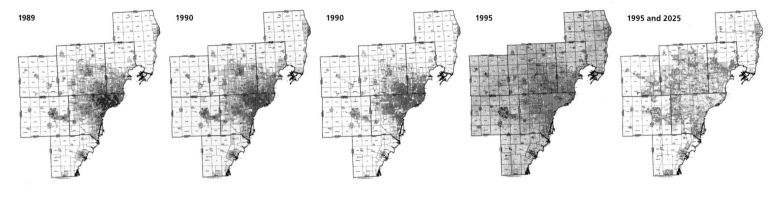

1989	1990	1990	1995	1995 and 2025
Households Without Personal Vehicle	**Households in Poverty**	**Older Population**	**Land Use/Land Cover**	**Land Development**

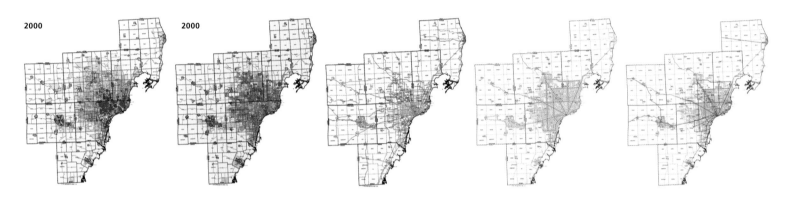

2000	2000			
Population Density	**Employment Density**	**Existing Fixed Transit Routes**	**Transit Supportive Areas**	**Proposed Transit Options**

Phase 1—Public Involvement

Southeast Michigan Council of Governments (SEMCOG)

Detroit, Michigan, USA

By Alex Bourgeau, Matt Carpenter, Xuan Liu, and Ann VanSlembrouck

Contact
Ann VanSlembrouck, vanslembrouck@semcog.org

Software
ArcView 3.2

Hardware
Pentium 4

Printer
HP DesignJet 1055CM

Data Source(s)
1990 U.S. census data and SEMCOG

GIS is helping to improve transit in southeast Michigan with a series of reference maps to assist in public education. A Transit Supportive Area map displays where public transit is needed. This area covers 71.7 percent of the employment in the region and 71.9 percent of the households in the region. The Proposed Transit Options map depicts opportunities, which will benefit the highest number of residents in the region.

Southeast Michigan Council of Governments

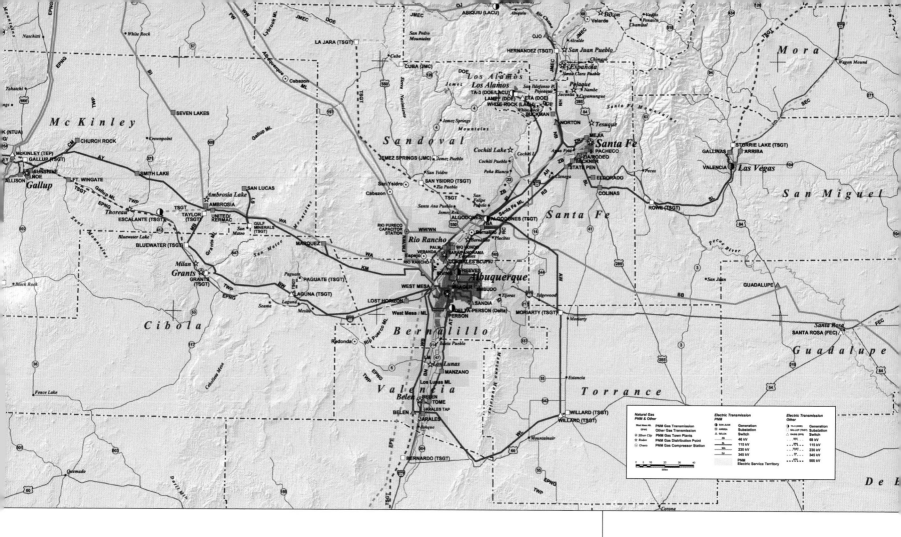

Public Service Company of New Mexico (PNM), in business since 1917, is the largest investor-owned gas and electric utility in New Mexico. The company serves 1.3 million people and is headquartered in Albuquerque.

Innovative Software Solutions (ISS) is a group within PNM that provides technologically innovative solutions to the company. ISS has developed engineering software to automate the design of electrical substations, a drawing archive and retrieval application, and a GIS-based system for management and maintenance of gas and electric transmission systems and provides Web development, engineering drafting, graphics, and three-dimensional modeling and visualization products. ISS is currently designing a geodatabase that incorporates much of PNM's geospatial assets that will be available within the company via a Spatial Database Engine™ (SDE®) server and custom ArcIMS applications.

The map illustrated here, a draft version of Major Transmission Systems in New Mexico, serves as a static front end for displaying a large portion of this data. The final version of the map, created in ArcView 8.1, is distributed throughout the company and to government regulating entities, other utilities, and the public.

Major Transmission Systems in New Mexico

Innovative Software Solutions, Public Service Company of New Mexico

Albuquerque, New Mexico, USA

By John Evaskovich

Contact

John Evaskovich, jevasko@pnm.com

Software

ArcView 8.1, ArcPress, Adobe Photoshop 6.0, and Windows 2000 Professional

Printer

HP DesignJet 5000

Data Source(s)

U.S. Geological Survey, New Mexico Resource Geographic Information System Program, global positioning system field data, and hard-copy maps from other companies

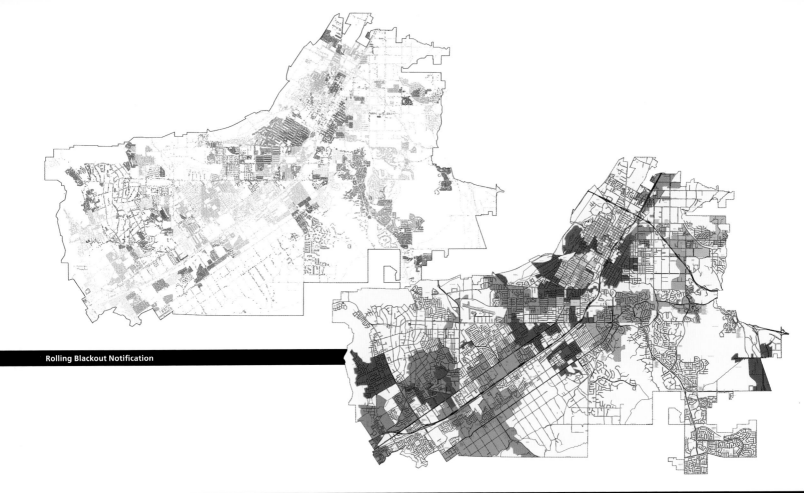

Blackout Notification by Circuit Number

Blackout Notifications

City of Riverside

Riverside, California, USA

By Robin Dyer *(Rolling Blackout)*
and Steven W. Lindelof *(by Circuit Number)*

Contact

Robin Dyer, rdyer@ci.riverside.ca.us

Steven Lindelof, slindelo@ci.riverside.ca.us

Software

ArcInfo 8.1

Hardware

Sun *(Rolling Blackout)* and Compaq DeskPro EN
(by Circuit Number)

Printer

HP DesignJet 755

Data Source(s)

City of Riverside GIS database

The City of Riverside Electric Utility supplies power to approximately 100,000 customers. The 2000 energy crisis in California prompted it to take steps that would help its customers prepare for possible blackouts.

Rolling Blackout Notification

The department wanted to place customers' electric block code on each bill. Customers are able to view their circuit areas and block codes on the city's Web site. Customer information and addresses are stored in a mainframe database (CIS). CIS has no knowledge of block codes, which comprise a group of electric circuits identified with a unique number. The circuit number is part of the GIS database but stored as a point attribute on transformer point features. The circuit number for a customer can change as crews perform maintenance and load balancing activities, and while the GIS is updated with this information, the CIS must have the ability to be regenerated monthly with updated circuit numbers and block codes. The solution was to download CIS data to the GIS, use ArcInfo geoprocessing to determine the circuit number and block code for each address, and then upload the resulting customer information back to the CIS with the block code attached. Because no attribute information is available to directly link the two data sets, all processing had to be done spatially.

Blackout Notification Areas by Circuit Number

Considering exempt circuits, a coverage was created to identify areas of electric blackout susceptibility. The coverage is based on the primary feeder circuits that supply power to areas in the city. A point coverage was created from the existing address point coverage, and the circuits that feed the address were appended to the table. The specific points were defined by the circuit numbers, and then parcels were selected on the given circuits. Based on the selected parcels for each circuit, circuit block areas were created to define the Blackout Notification Areas in Riverside.

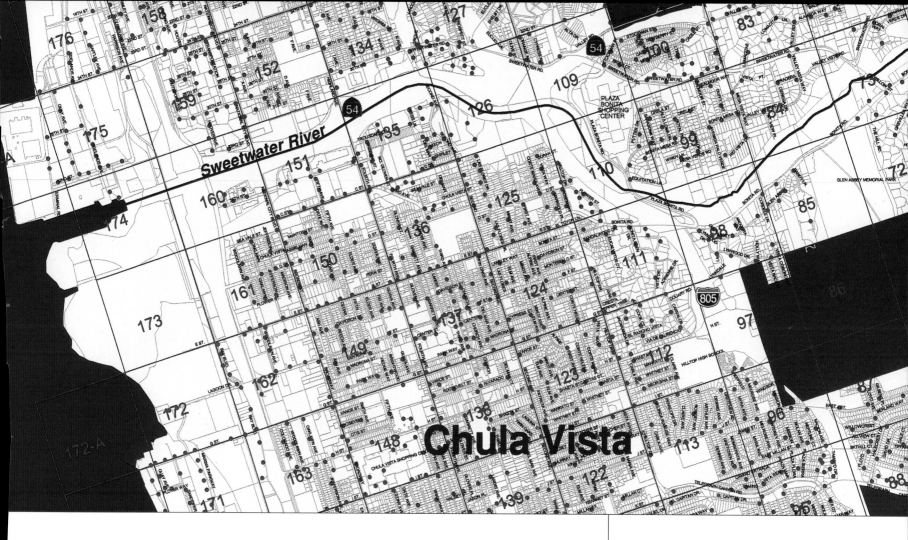

Sweetwater Authority, a publicly owned water agency, is the third largest water retailer in San Diego County, California. The authority serves a population of more than 175,000 residents in the South Bay. The 32-square-mile service area includes National City, the western half of the City of Chula Vista, and Bonita (San Diego County).

Sweetwater Authority's system includes 384 miles of distribution pipe and more than 33,000 service connections. The authority owns and operates Loveland Reservoir near Alpine, California; the Sweetwater Reservoir in Spring Valley, California; a brackish groundwater demineralization facility in Chula Vista; and deep freshwater wells in National City.

With the exception of private fire hydrants, Sweetwater Authority maintains all of the fire hydrants within the service area. Four years ago, the authority established a program to track the maintenance of the fire hydrants. An Access database was created that contains two tables—a location table and a maintenance table. The primary key in both tables is the fire hydrant number, and every fire hydrant in the system is assigned a unique number. Currently, the location table consists of 2,417 fire hydrants. The maintenance data displayed in this ArcView map was generated from the data collected by the Sweetwater Authority Fire Hydrant Maintenance Crew. Inset maps give management a visual of all areas that were maintained (or not maintained) during a given year.

Sweetwater Authority's Fire Hydrant Maintenance Program
Sweetwater Authority

Chula Vista, California, USA

By Debra Stein

Contact
Debra Stein, dstein@sweetwater.org

Software
ArcView, Microsoft Access, Microsoft Excel, dBASE, Corel Photo-Paint 9, and Windows NT

Hardware
Pentium II

Printer
HP DesignJet 3500CP

Data Source(s)
Sweetwater Authority, San Diego Geographic Information Source, and San Diego Association of Governments

Sweetwater Authority

Legend
- ⬤ ALTERNATIVE 4 - MODIFY REGULATING WEIR
- ○ ALTERNATIVE 7 - INSTALL REGULATING WEIR
- ⬠ COMBINED SEWER OVERFLOW
- ⊕ ALTERNATIVE 5 - PROVIDE OFF-LINE STORAGE
- ○ MODEL NODE
- — MODELED SEWER NETWORK
- ▢ SUBCATCHMENT MINIBASIN
- ▨ ALTERNATIVE 1 - ONGING SEWER SEPARATION
- ▨ ALTERNATIVE 1a - PLANNED SEWER SEPARATION

Buffalo Sewer Authority

O'Brien and Gere Engineers, Inc.

Williamsville, New York, USA

By William Bosse

Contact
William Bosse, bossewf@obg.com

Software
ArcView 3.2a, ArcMap 8.1, XP-SWMM 6.1, AutoCAD LT 2000i, Corel Photo House 2.1, Microsoft Access, and Windows NT

Hardware
Compaq DeskPro workstation

Printer
HP DesignJet 650C

Data Source(s)
Buffalo Sewer Authority, New York State aerial orthophotos, and collected raw data

Like many cities throughout the northeast, Buffalo has a combined sewer system. During wet weather events, excessive flows within the sewer system are relieved through combined sewer overflows (CSO). The Buffalo Sewer Authority is required, under its State Pollution Discharge Elimination System Permit, to develop a long-term control plan for CSO abatement, which will implement the best management practices and ultimately comply with the Clean Water Act. To that end, a hydrologic model, delineating and characterizing sewer watershed areas, was developed and used to predict wet weather runoff entering the collection system during rainfall events. A hydraulic model, representing relevant pipes and combined sewer regulators, was also developed and used to route flows through the collection system network.

Extensive field data collection activities verified and characterized the physical attributes of the existing system and were used for comparison to historical data. Data from flow monitors and staff gauges was collected and evaluated continuously over a five-month period. Tipping bucket rain gauges were used to segregate weather events and to analyze subcatchment-specific response characteristics. During defined weather events, water quality samples were collected throughout the collection system at CSOs and receiving water bodies.

This map is part of a series developed to support a memorandum prepared by O'Brien and Gere Engineers, which discussed long-term control objectives for the north district of the Buffalo Sewer Authority's service area and analyzed the existing collection system incorporating various specified CSO design alternatives. The maps thematically display the modeled design alternatives.

O'Brien and Gere Engineers, Inc.